ABOUT THIS GUIDE

Planning to build? is a practical guide to the processes involved in a building project.

READERSHIP

Planning to build? is written for an intending client of the construction industry, that is, one who will be responsible for commissioning and paying for building work. It is intended particularly for those approaching the industry for the first time, or with only limited knowledge of what is involved.

For simplicity and clarity, the client is often addressed in this guide as "you", or referred to as "he"; in practice the client may equally be male, female or a corporate entity.

CONTENT

Planning to build? offers a step-by-step introduction to the activities needed to take a building project from initial idea through to the take-over of completed work. It outlines the different 'procurement routes' that can be followed, and the considerations that should influence which option to choose.

HOW TO USE THIS GUIDE

Planning to build? describes the roles and responsibilities of the key contributors to the process. It is especially intended to enable you, the client, to understand and play your part in what might be a complex and demanding undertaking.

The guide has been structured so that it can be used both by those who wish to read it from cover to cover and by those who simply need to 'dip in' for specific information or to keep ahead of events as the scheme develops. It is divided into sections that focus on key issues:

SECTION 1 **THE CONSTRUCTION INDUSTRY TODAY**
....introduces the different approaches to construction in the UK, and the implications for clients of recent changes in the industry. The roles of the main participants are described and defined as they are used in this guide.

SECTION 2 **BEING A CLIENT**
....*is essential reading for the potential client.* It identifies the responsibilities of this role and some of the tasks that must be performed by the client if the project is to be successful

SECTION 3 **GETTING STARTED; ENGAGING ADVISERS**
....outlines the practicalities of getting started. It identifies the need for an initial appraisal to establish a project strategy, before discussing the key first step of selecting and appointing advisers.

SECTION 4 **FROM IDEA TO OCCUPATION**
....explains the tasks common to all construction projects

SECTION 5 **CHOICES - THE CRITERIA**
....examines the competing priorities to be taken into account when considering the choice of procurement route.

SECTION 6 **CHOICES: THE OPTIONS**
....describes the most commonly used procurement options. Each is reviewed with its variants, discussing key features, relationships, roles, advantages and disadvantages.

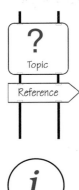

Appendices provide definitions, detailed check lists and other useful information.

By reading only the first three sections, even the busiest would-be client can quickly gain an understanding of the essentials necessary to getting started. From that point you should be able to decide whether to spend further time on the more detailed reading that follows or delegate this to someone else with a remit to report back on the action needed.

Some words have specific meanings, which are summarised in Appendix 1. These are shown in *italics* when first used in each section. Marginal symbols, as shown left, are used throughout for ease of cross referencing.

Further and more detailed information may be obtained through reference to other publications noted in the bibliography. The marginal 'information' symbol is used to indicate where this is the case.

IS THIS GUIDE ALL THAT IS NEEDED?

No single guide can anticipate the circumstances and demands of all possible building projects. *'Planning to build'* is intended to enable the client to see the big picture, ask relevant questions, and commission the necessary expert help and advice to provide specific answers. It will empower the client to participate effectively in the process.

Other publications, especially other guides published by CIRIA, provide more detailed information on specific issues.

WHAT ARE THE KEY WATCH POINTS?

Reading this guide should help you to understand:

- the importance of keeping control of what is going on at a strategic level; some delegation is possible but the final authority is yours
- the need to ensure that the project is always given adequate resources; time, effort (and money) are handsomely rewarded
- the value of appointing the most appropriate advisers who will work successfully with you (and with each other)
- the importance of honest and explicit communication through clearly defined roles
- the enormous benefits of genuine teamwork
- the importance of providing as much and as accurate information as possible
- that problems arise from indecision or changes of mind
- that the process will sometimes be difficult and unpleasant as well as rewarding

For many clients building is simply a means to an end, just another task to be completed. Anyone considering embarking on building works for the first time should not underestimate the demands that they will make or the crucial importance of the client's own part. If, as client, you can spend time only on the bare essentials, you will want know what these are and what arrangements you will need to make so that all the client functions are nevertheless carried out effectively. *Planning to build?*

suggests which tasks can be delegated and which must remain your personal responsibility.

ACKNOWLEDGEMENTS

This publication was funded by:

DEPARTMENT OF THE ENVIRONMENT
NATIONAL CONTRACTORS GROUP OF THE BUILDING EMPLOYERS CONFEDERATION
NATIONAL WESTMINSTER BANK

The guide was written and illustrated by:

MALCOLM POTTER AA dipl RIBA,

acting as CIRIA's Research Contractor for the project. The final draft was prepared with editorial assistance from:

CAROLINE HOGARTH, BA.

The work was overseen by a Steering Group comprising:

B J CORFE, FCIOB	Tysons PLC (representing the National Contractors Group of the Building Employers Confederation)
T W FORSYTH, AA dipl., RIBA	D Y Davies International Ltd
D V GARDINER, FRICS	Property Services Agency (Retired)
PROF R HOWES, MPhil, PhD, MCIOB (Chairman)	South Bank University
R F KENNEDY	Building Employers Confederation
S A MURRAY, BSc, ACGI, CEng	Ove Arup and Partners
I M NEEDLE, MSc, FRICS	National Westminster Bank PLC
C PARSLOE, BSc, CEng, MCIBSE	Building Services Research and Information Association
P WILSON, DBA, MBA, MSE, RIBA	The Centre for Consultancy (London) Ltd
P B WOODHEAD, BEng, CEng, MICE	Department of the Environment

Valuable assistance was also provided by:

C SOLMAN	Ford Motor Company
J PRICE, LLB	Building Employers Confederation
W CROSBIE-HILL, FRICS	

The project was managed by CIRIA's Research Manager for Management Topics:

A JACKSON-ROBBINS, BSC, MCIOB.

CIRIA acknowledges with gratitude the contribution made by all of the above.

CONTENTS

1
THE CONSTRUCTION INDUSTRY TODAY

This section outlines the background to the construction industry and introduces the roles and responsibilities of the main participants.

2
BEING A CLIENT

This section is essential reading for the potential client; it identifies the responsibilities of this role and some of the tasks that must be performed by the client if the project is to be successful.

3
GETTING STARTED, ENGAGING ADVISERS

This section describes the processes required to select and appoint the key players and enable the start of a project.

4
FROM IDEA TO OCCUPATION

This section describes the processes applicable to all construction projects, whatever the chosen method of procurement.

5

CHOICES - THE CRITERIA

This section identifies some of the key issues that need to be considered in making the choice about the most appropriate procurement route for your project.

6

CHOICES - THE OPTIONS

This section sets out the principle procurement options. It describes the main arrangements and characteristics of each, including their advantages and disadvantages.

APPENDICES

FIGURES

SECTION 1
THE CONSTRUCTION
INDUSTRY TODAY

This section outlines the backround to the construction industry and introduces the roles and responsibilities of the main participants.

APPROACHES TO CONSTRUCTION

THE TRADITIONAL ROUTE

The origins of today's construction industry lie in the industrial expansion of the nineteenth century, when the designer-led arrangement became the established approach to building. The designer, usually an *architect* or *engineer*, would be appointed first to take the *clients* instructions and draw up the necessary plans and *specifications*. The *builder* would then be appointed to carry out the work, to the instructions of the designer. This route is still widely followed.

OTHER ROUTES

In recent years some features of the traditional route, such as the strict compartmentalising of design and construction, have led to problems as projects became more complex and demanding. Other approaches have been developed, to meet the demands of clients for greater flexibility and accountability. A number of routes can now be taken in the *procurement* of building work, and these can be considered in two broad categories:

(i) those which feature 'multipoint' accountability to the client, with individual organisations separately responsible for particular aspects of design and for construction.

(ii) those which provide single point accountability, with a single organisation assuming responsibility for all aspects of both design and construction

This guide outlines the procurement routes now available, their key features, and the criteria that you can apply in choosing between them.

THE ORGANISATION OF THE INDUSTRY

THE STRUCTURE OF THE INDUSTRY

Commercial forces and technological advance have also driven changes in the structure and organisation of the industry, and in the range of services offered by individual firms. Longstanding assumptions may no longer be valid and clients must consider carefully the services required, and how these are best provided.

Many of the larger building companies no longer have a directly employed workforce of trades-people; instead they rely upon subcontractors. Increasingly the builder's role is changing from that of direct provider to manager and coordinator.

While consultant *advisers* have traditionally been independent, offering services within a single discipline, many are now able to provide multidisciplinary services, either 'in-house' or through consortium arrangements with other practices. New skills are being recognised, such as *risk management* and *value management*; these are available both from new breeds of specialist and as an extension of the services offered by firms already established in older disciplines.

Collaboration between builders, design practices and other consultant advisers is increasingly common, to offer the client an all-in service covering both design and construction.

Many buildings now contain complex mechanical and electrical services and for these the *building services engineer* is an essential member of the design team. Similarly, specialist contractors in this and other areas are now key members of the building team, offering design as well as construction services within their specialisation. The coordination of such specialist work into the design and construction process is an increasingly critical task.

Many clients acknowledge the need for a *project manager* for the often formidable task of coordinating a building project. Project management is now a recognised skill, supported by formal training. Project managers come from a range of professional backgrounds. In addition to specialist firms, many builders and consultant advisers now offer project management in addition to their mainstream skills.

TRAINING, QUALIFICATION AND QUALITY ASSURANCE

The service given by any firm on your project will reflect the quality of the people they employ. The professional institutions within the industry set standards for training and qualification and require an all-round standard of proficiency, including a minimum level of practical experience.

In addition to personal qualification of staff, many firms have obtained certification against BS EN ISO 9000 (BS 5750) 'Quality management systems'. Although this does not set standards for the building work itself, it is intended to ensure the maintenance of consistent standards by creating a positive procedural framework.

STANDARD DOCUMENTATION

Many of the procedures associated with the well-established procurement routes are supported by industry standard documents. In particular, a range of standard forms of contract are available for construction works, together with forms of appointment for consultant advisers.

The use, without amendment, of an appropriate standard form has clear advantages, in terms of familiarity to the industry and established case law. However, the implications of various forms are being debated in the light of changing circumstances in the industry. You should examine carefully any proposed contract or agreement, with the benefit of expert advice, to be satisfied it matches your needs and expectations for your project.

ROLES AND FUNCTIONS

This guide describes the key roles in the building process by reference to the functions performed, rather then the professions of those who normally (but not necessarily) perform them. Those most commonly referred to are listed below; a more comprehensive description of 'whos's who' is given in appendix 1. In this guide, the term 'adviser' is used for any firm or individual providing advice, information or design services.

The essential functions remain the same whatever the procurement route, but there are wide differences in relationships and the ways in which roles are fulfilled. Particular roles are examined in more detail in Section 6 in the context of different procurement procedures.

THE CLIENT

The client is the person or organisation using and paying for services. In most standard forms of contract the client is referred to as the employer. The client may be represented by others, for example:

CLIENT'S REPRESENTATIVE

The *client's representative* is usually (but not necessarily) a member of the clients' own organisation, providing a well-informed day-to-day link with the project. The appointment of a client's representative does not relieve you of the responsibility to take decisions and control the job.

EMPLOYER'S AGENT

The employer's agent is a construction adviser employed to act as the client's agent in a contract with a design and build organisation.

PROJECT MANAGER

A project manager may be engaged by the client to coordinate and manage the entire process from inception to completion. This can include everything from arranging the initial appointments of the design team to managing the occupation of the completed building. The project management role is usually most effective when it is not combined with other roles and is therefore unaffected by potential conflicts of interest. The project manager's responsibility has to be defined for each project and he must be given effective authority.

However, on a small or straightforward project, where an independent project manager has not been appointed it is common for some aspects of the project management function to be combined with other functions such as:

- Client's representative
- *Design team leader*
- *Construction manager*

DESIGNERS

Designers, often referred to as design consultants include:

- Architects
- *Surveyors*
- *Structural engineers*
- Building services engineers
- *Landscape architects*
- *Technology specialists*

Designers of different disciplines may be individually employed by the client, or work for a multi-disciplinary organisation with which he has a single contract. Even when separately employed, they have to work together as a design team to produce an integrated design.

DESIGN TEAM LEADER

This is the lead designer responsible for managing and coordinating the work of the design team so that it meets the client's requirements, including the budget and time schedules.

CONTRACT ADMINISTRATOR OR SUPERVISING OFFICER

These are terms used in standard forms of contract for the person who administers the building contract on the client's behalf. In most cases the design team leader takes on this role.

COST ADVISER

The *cost adviser* advises on building costs and estimating.

The cost adviser can have two distinct roles:

* as an integral part of the design team providing cost advice to them, and to the client.
* directly appointed to advise the client generally about costs and value, separate from the design team.

Where the cost adviser is a part of the design team he is responsible for the quality of the advice he gives but not for the management of the project budget; this is the responsibility of the design team leader or project manager.

The cost adviser is usually a *quantity surveyor* but on very small projects a separate appointment cannot always be justified and the designer takes on the role.

BUILDER The builder takes responsibility for providing and coordinating the construction work. In this guide the term includes:

* any general construction company
* management contractors

Other terms are used where the function comprises or includes other roles, as follows.

CONTRACTOR A contractor is any organisation or individual who contracts to carry out defined services. 'Contractor' is the term used to describe the builder under most standard forms of building contract.

DESIGN AND BUILD ORGANISATION Design and build organisations provide a design service in addition to a construction capability. They are usually construction companies, either with a design capability in house or in consortium with a designer.

SUPPLIER Suppliers only supply materials or equipment. Their work is erected or installed by others. Suppliers may provide advice or a design service to the design team.

SUBCONTRACTOR Subcontractors carry out defined elements of construction work for the builder, usually of a specialist trade such as roofing or heating and ventilation. Subcontractors may design these elements and may also manufacture and supply the materials or equipment that they erect or install on site.

WORKS CONTRACTOR/ TRADE CONTRACTOR These are contractors who undertake packages of construction work under the *management contracting* and *construction management* procurement methods.

OTHERS
CLERK OF WORKS A clerk of works or inspector checks the quality of construction on site. He works closely with the design team leader but is usually directly employed by the client.

FACILITIES MANAGER The facilities manager is responsible for the efficient running of the completed building and equipment. He may have a key role in compiling the brief, and at handover and occupation of the building.

6

SECTION 2
BEING A CLIENT

This section is essential reading for the potential client; it identifies the responsibilities of this important role and some of the tasks that must be performed by the client if the project is to be successful.

APPROACHING THE PROJECT

A successful building is one which meets the *client's* needs and expectations.

Success in building depends as much on real cooperation from all the people involved as the technical method by which it is achieved. Whatever skills are invested in a project, they will be really effective only if brought together in a spirit of genuine teamwork.

As client you will take the lead in the team and in forming partnerships with the other players. Always remember that this is your project - and that you must keep control of it.

You will face risks and carry responsibilities, and you must weigh carefully the demands they will make on you. Your attitude to risk and responsibility will be a key factor in deciding which *procurement route* you will follow and the forms of contract you will use.

ACCEPTING RESPONSIBILITIES

Every construction project involves at least two separate organisations and usually many more. For things to go smoothly the roles of each must be clearly defined - and then adhered to. The role and responsibilities of the client are described below. Tasks can be delegated, but there are some that only you as client can perform. The clients duties are summarised in figure 2.1, with an indication of the extent and nature of possible delegation.

In practice, the client's role can impose considerable demands upon individuals and organisations. Failure to carry out duties can not only put the client in breach of contract but also jeopardize the success of the project.

KNOWING THE OBJECTIVES The objectives for the new project need to be absolutely clear. Before approaching *advisers* it is worth putting on paper key things that are required of the finished building. Good advisers want to start from basics and question all the assumptions that have been made. They will be looking for the best answer to the problems and may well come up with entirely new ideas. So keep an open mind and be receptive to alternative solutions.

INTERNAL ARRANGEMENTS To avoid confusion about instructions for the project, there must be a single point of contact through whom all information and decisions are channelled. This might be the client personally on a straightforward project. Otherwise, someone with sufficient time and skills must be found to act as project executive or *client's representative*. A full-time commitment is often required on major projects, for at least the setting-up stages. If there is nobody available within the client's organisation, somebody from outside must be engaged. In either case, the client's representative must always have quick and direct access to the decision-making process.

SELECTING ADVISERS The selection and appointment of advisers is one of the most crucial client tasks. Time and effort spent on the initial selection and terms of appointment will be well repaid. Above all, you must be confident that you can work together even when things get difficult.

SETTING PRIORITIES It will be necessary to balance difficult or conflicting priorities. Important strategic choices will be required at an early stage.

PREPARING A BRIEF In addition to understanding the broad aims of the project, your advisers need to be briefed with as much detailed information as possible. They will want to know, for example, what the building will be used for, any special requirements of those who will occupy it, or of the processes they will carry out. They will also need to know how the project will be financed, the size of the budget and how much will be available and when. Your building will be only as good as your *brief*. Preparation is difficult and time-consuming, but time and effort at this stage will pay dividends later.

...AND MAKING DECISIONS The brief will be developed and refined in iterative discussions with your advisers, in which you must decide on options offered in response to your basic requirements. Establish cut-off points for making your decisions and stick to them. Provide further information when required; advisors who have to guess are liable to guess wrong. Late changes of mind can cause delay and extra cost.

LISTENING TO THE USERS Make sure that those who will use the building have a timely input into the brief, particularly if they are specialists requiring a particular environment. Both they and the building will work better if their advice is sought.

In any case, a building project can be very disruptive and disturbing. Even if people are not directly affected by the noise and dust of the building operations, they may have to move to temporary or new accommodation. They will be happier if they are consulted, and kept informed from the beginning.

FUNDING AND PAYMENTS Payments are likely to fall into two broad categories:
- fees to advisers - usually paid by instalments in arrears and related to the stage of the work completed
- payments for construction work - either in agreed stages or against *certificates* issued by the *contract administrator*.

The client must have funding in place in order to pay promptly and within the agreed timescales. Those who are being paid will already have had to fund the work themselves.

If payments are made against certificates, these will take account of all the items for which payments are due. This means they will take account not only outstanding money for completed work but also any other items such as legitimate contractual *claims*. The payment will also exclude any costs where deductions are appropriate, as in the case of defective work.

MONITORING PROGRESS AND COSTS Your advisers will assist in proposing and administering the necessary contractual arrangements, but it is you the client who will enter the contracts and who will accept the obligations they impose.

One of a client's key tasks is watching that the project stays within the agreed budget and timescales. Cost management and progress monitoring are not the responsibility only of paid advisers. The client must keep fully abreast of what is going on by insisting on full and regular reports. Always remember that your own actions, particularly late decisions or changes, can have a big impact on the project.

FACING RISKS

New clients need to be aware from the outset that building, like any complex enterprise, involves risks. Construction projects are particularly susceptible to those which manifest themselves in time and cost over-runs. Setting up an arbitrary contingency fund is a poor - and potentially impoverishing - substitute for clear analysis and careful management of risk.

RISKS IN CONSTRUCTION

A number of crucial factors can change during the sometimes long life of a building project. Significant risk areas might include:

- government regulations
- funding /fiscal arrangements
- scope of project
- adequacy of design to meet requirements
- local conditions, climate, familiarity, accessibility
- construction market - companies, materials, labour
- estimating data
- inflation - exchange rates.

All of these can and frequently do affect the outcome of a contract but are not always adequately recognised when the project starts.

Working with your advisers you must identify the major risk areas in your project, and agree a strategy for dealing with them.

MANAGING RISK

Quite naturally, most projects begin in an atmosphere of common enthusiasm. From expert to novice, the aim is to get the job going and deal with the problems later. Naive optimism is seldom justified. All participants need to be level-headed, look realistically at every feature of the project and plan accordingly.

The client can take the lead here by:

- taking trouble over the appointment of advisers
- requesting and considering objective advice, even if unwelcome.
- giving time and thought to the brief
- accepting realistic targets
- keeping abreast via regular reports of progress particularly with respect to time and cost
- making timely decisions and sticking to them - change and uncertainty are the greatest individual causes of things going wrong
- insisting on value rather than merely the lowest price
- adopting with your advisers a systematic approach to the analysis and management of risk.

Risks in construction

See Sections 5 & 6

You must choose a procurement route that is appropriate to the risk you wish to carry, and ensure that any proposed contract or agreement reflects your wishes and intentions.

IN CASE OF DISPUTE A well-considered project carried out in a spirit of partnership is the best insurance against things going wrong. It is nevertheless wise to be sure that you are as well protected as you can be against such an eventuality. In principle, a client may have redress against any or all of the organisations with whom he has contracted, designers, *builders* or other parties.

The rights and obligations of the client are laid down in the various contracts and agreements he enters into. It is therefore extremely important to use appropriate forms. Take care to obtain balanced, objective advice.

All reputable designers carry *professional indemnity* insurance. This should cover them for any act of negligence or other failure in their expert duties. When making an appointment, it is important to enquire about what is covered and whether there are any limitations which could affect your right of redress. The designer's obligation is to act with normal professional competence; this does not extend to warranting 'fitness for purposes' of their design.

The project arrangements must cover any specialist items designed by subcontractors or suppliers, to ensure that responsibility is taken for any defects or failure to achieve performance. It is also essential that there is clearly defined responsibility for coordinating the design of specialist items with each other and with the main building elements.

The standard forms of contract for building work include various mechanisms for resolving disputes. Most provide for arbitration, although some allow for prompt adjudication as work proceeds. Formal arbitration can be costly and protracted; negotiation is usually considerably more effective and less expensive, especially if it takes place before a dispute builds up into confrontation

MANAGING THE PROJECT

The client's contribution to the project must be effectively managed. This could be the responsibility of the client's representative, who must be given appropriate authority. The clients representative might also manage the project as a whole.

If the necessary time and skills are not available to the client's representative, you should consider appointing a *project manager.*

HEALTH AND SAFETY OBLIGATIONS

The Construction (Design & Management) Regulations 1994 impose a number of duties on clients with regard to health and safety on site during the construction of the project. The main thrust of the Regulations is to require designers to ensure that their designs can be constructed and maintained safely.

Particular duties on clients (or their agents) are as follows:

- to appoint a competent Planning Supervisor, who will coordinate health and safety matters during the design stage
- to appoint a competent Principal Contractor, who will coordinate health and safety matters during the construction phase
- to be satisfied that the Planning Supervisor, Principal Contractor and other designers and contractors working on the project, are competent and will allocate adequate resources to perform their functions as defined in the Regulations
- to provide the planning Supervisor with relevant health and safety information for the project
- to ensure construction work does not start until a satisfactory 'Health and Safety' plan has been prepared
- to declare to the Health and Safety Executive the name and address of the client or agent for the project and the address of the site
- to ensure the 'Health and Safety File' produced for the project can be inspected at a later stage e.g. prior to maintenance or refurbishment.

There are some exclusions regarding the size of project to which the Regulations apply and there are certain types of project for which not all the Regulations need to be considered.

You should seek guidance on how these Regulations affect you.

FIGURE 2.1

SUMMARY OF CLIENT'S OWN TASKS

CLIENT RESPONSIBILITY	EXTENT OF DELEGATION		DELEGATED TASKS
Identify Objectives	●●●●●		Nil delegation
Make internal arrangements	●●●●	●	Facilitate
Appoint Advisers	●●●	●●	Assist with selection and interview
Set Priorities	●●●●	●	Provide advice and options
Provide information prepare brief	●	●●●●	Coordinate and liaise
Make decisions, accept risks	●●●●	●	Report and advise on options
Liaise with users	●	●●●●	Arrange and coordinate
Arrange funding	●●●	●●	Arrange payments
Enter contract	●●	●●●	Arrange advice on contents and warranties
Monitor progress and costs	●	●●●●	Day to day detailed monitoring

SECTION 3
GETTING STARTED, ENGAGING ADVISERS

This section describes the processes required to select and appoint the key players and enable the start of a project.

INITIAL APPRAISAL

REASONS FOR BUILDING

For success, buildings should fit around the way we want to work. Change and development in your organisation will change your accommodation needs. It is essential that you look carefully at your reasons for planning to build, and how your needs are best met, now and in the future. You might:

- reshape and refurbish your existing building
- adapt a building elsewhere
- procure a new, purpose-built facility.

OBTAINING INITIAL ADVICE

Almost certainly you will need help in identifying and weighing the basic options for your project. This advice must be balanced and objective; there are potential advantages in speaking to someone who would have no interest in the project proceeding in a particular way (or at all).

You should seek advice from those who can understand your requirements, as well as knowing about building. Advice might be available 'in-house' from a colleague with relevant experience, otherwise from an outside organisation. Writing down and prioritising your reasons for building might point to an appropriate source, for example:

- developing a site as an investment suggests financial or property advice
- altering an historic building for any purpose demands sound knowledge of old buildings, for both structural and 'heritage' considerations.

Seek advice from organisations that have broad and relevant experience, and an appropriate range of skills. Be fully prepared for the consultation; it helps to provide in advance a summary of the project objectives and the main questions to be covered.

THE BASIC QUESTIONS

At this early stage answers are needed to some very basic questions:

- what type of building work will best meet my needs ?
- how complex will the project be ?
- approximately how much will it cost ?
- which *procurement route* appears most suitable ?
- what sort of team will be needed to progress the project ?

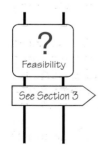

You must have a basic project strategy in place, based on broad answers to those important questions, before entering into any serious fee or other commitment for a specific scheme. Give careful consideration to the need for a *feasibility study* before proceeding any further.

ENGAGING ADVISERS

BASIC REQUIREMENTS

Different qualities and skills may be required of your *advisers* at successive stages of a project. In particular, objectivity and the ability to take a broad view are essential requirements when giving initial advice or carrying out a feasibility study; more specific expertise will be required once the project strategy has been identified and the client is in a position to go ahead. Accordingly appointments to provide initial advice or to carry out a feasibility study should be for that phase of the work only.

The nature of the project and the procurement route will determine the skills required in the team of advisers and the order in which they are appointed. For example:

- if the quality of design is paramount, and you have chosen the *designer-led* procurement option, the designer is the most important person with whom to start

- if value for money is a key issue and you are intending to employ a *design-and-build organisation*, an appropriately experienced *cost adviser* would be a good starting point

- if the project is likely to be technically demanding or require complex coordination, a *project manager* might be the best first port of call.

The first appointment should be the principal adviser who can take the project forward and help with the selection of the others specialists.

THE SELECTION PROCESS

Selecting advisers who are right for you and for your project is essential to success. This means you must first identify your needs and match them with the most appropriate services on offer. The process should be systematic and as objective as possible, but it will inevitably require the exercise of judgement.

Balancing the quality of service against the cost of fees is potentially difficult; detailed guidance is available in the CIRIA guide 'Value by competition'. However, for the newcomer careful selection based primarily on interview, followed by negotiation of fees, may be the best arrangement.

Your selection criteria will depend on your requirements, but you should always aim to appoint advisers who will have a positive, team-oriented attitude. It is important to choose firms whose skills and experience suit the project and in whose approach you have both confidence and sympathy.

INITIAL SELECTION

There are several sources of information that can help with the initial selection of advisers:

- the professional bodies and trade associations have directories of their members; some offer advisory services to the public
- local planning authorities and public libraries often have lists of local firms and directories
- other clients who regularly undertake building work may be prepared to offer advice.

WANT AN EXTENSION ?
Take great care over briefing and who you choose to do the design!

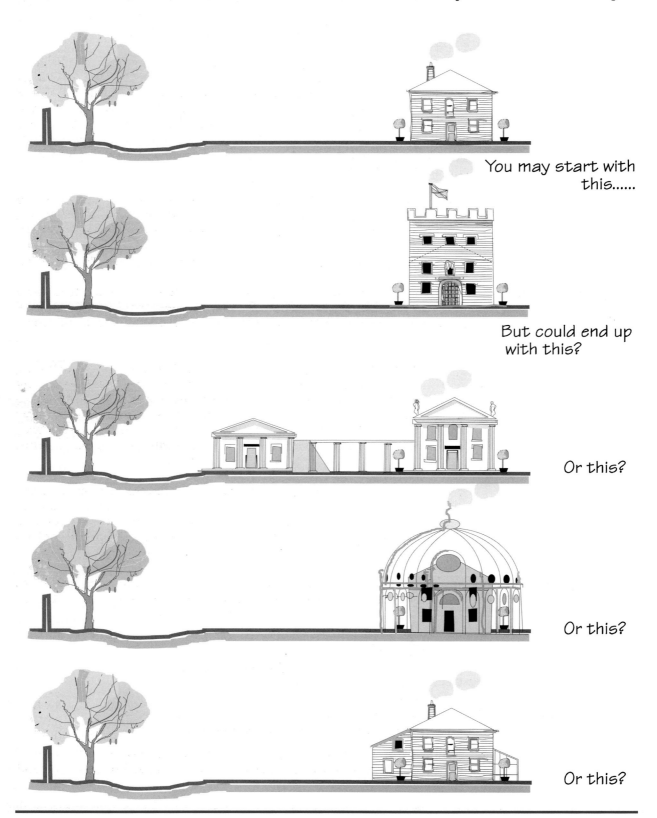

You may start with this......

But could end up with this?

Or this?

Or this?

Or this?

Having listed about a dozen candidates, obtain a copy of each company's brochure including a summary of their organisation and examples of recent work. These not only give a good idea of the house style but should show the depth of experience and range of skills available. They will also probably give the names of current and previous clients.

One of the most useful ways of finding out more about a firm is to talk to other clients who have already worked with them. Experience often varies so it is worth talking to at least two or three separate clients who have worked with the same firm. A check list is useful in ensuring the same questions are asked of each so valid comparisons can be made. Find out too, if possible, the names of the people who took part in each project. When the final choice is made you will want to have some say in who it is that you will be working with.

Is a local or national firm appropriate? Location is likely to be an important consideration if the project is relatively small or within a particularly 'sensitive' area. It is perfectly reasonable to include both local and national companies in your short-list for interview and to discuss with them how they would deal with any important local issues.

FINAL SELECTION When making the final selection, it is usual to see between three and six firms. For the selection interview you will need to prepare an outline of your requirements and a standard set of questions about the firm's experience and organisation.

At the interview each firm presents its approach to the project, including an indication of its proposed fees. Use this opportunity to ask searching questions. If a range of skills are needed at this stage, it is important to meet all the main people who will represent these and to find out how they propose to work together. Above all you must satisfy yourself that the people you finally choose are in sympathy with your ideas and that you feel comfortable and can work well with them.

Before finally making up your mind visit, if you can, the office of the chosen firm. This often helps to confirm whether the claims made at interview are true. When the choice has been made notify everyone quickly and get down to agreeing the details of the principal appointment(s).

MAKING THE APPOINTMENT However informal you may like your working relationships to be it is vital that there is a clear definition of the responsibilities that each party carries and the terms on which they do so.

You need to agree:

- what services you are contracting to buy
- the basis of remuneration
- when payment is due
- the length of the contract
- how to end it and on what conditions.

Coming to grips with this need not be too daunting, as any newly selected adviser will be equally anxious to ensure that there is a clear understanding. A written agreement which sets out the conditions of appointment is essential. Standard forms of agreement are available; these have the advantage of familiarity in the industry, but you should ensure that they match your requirements. Go through the proposed agreement thoroughly with your adviser before signing, so that for example you are really clear which services are provided for the agreed fee, and which are not. Look ahead to the need to engage other advisers, and to place contracts with a *builder* and possibly specialists advisers and installers. If necessary, take independent advice on any points that concern you, and to ensure that the obligations of all parties in the project fit together.

BASIS OF FEES   In recent years the fees of consultant advisers have become much more subject to market conditions, and any fee levels quoted by professional bodies are now for guidance only. However, it remains in the client's interests to ensure that fee levels are reasonable for the adviser as well as for himself. The appropriate level for a particular appointment can be checked by enquiries of other clients, and finally agreed in negotiations.

The total cost of fees tends to be proportionally lower for larger projects and higher for more sophisticated or difficult schemes. The tender in a design and build or other arrangement with *single point* responsibility to the client will include design fees. However, subject to market conditions, the total cost of such services are likely to be much the same as those that would be incurred under procurement options involving *multipoint* responsibility.

Fees can be charged in a number of ways:

- 'ad valorem', that is, a percentage of the construction cost: this has been the most familiar basis, but is not now seen as the most appropriate by many clients

- hourly time-charge: necessary when it is not possible to quantify in advance the commitment of the adviser

- 'lump-sum', fixed fee arrangement: this offers advantages to the client, but is feasible only if the service required can be anticipated and specified in detail.

Lump sum and ad valorem fee agreements should include a basis for time charges to cover work outside the basic service. These can be expensive and unpredictable so be clear about the circumstances when they are likely to be used, and establish the methods by which your advisers obtain your authority for working in this way. One of the best solutions is to set an agreed budget which cannot be exceeded without your written permission.

Some expenses such as travel, printing and other incidental costs are frequently not included in the basic fee agreement, and are thus charged separately. You will need to agree a realistic budget for these costs, which again should not be exceeded without your authority.

GETTING GOING

Once appointments have been made, a first priority will be to establish the working arrangements between you and your adviser(s). These should include:

- points of contact - identify names on all sides
- methods for authorising critical decisions
- work plans and methods and frequency for updating
- information requirements - all parties
- record keeping and distribution
- the management and frequency of meetings.

It is essential to set up domestic arrangements to meet the demands that the project will undoubtedly make. Who is to to be the *clients representative* to provide the day to day management from your end ? Has that person the resources, time and authority to do the job efficiently ? Is any other help needed ?

As you consider each stage, make a note of the things you feel you need to know more about. It is essential that you understand what is going on and questioning is an essential part of the process, particularly when your requirements are being developed and the main events of the new project mapped out.

20

SECTION 4

FROM IDEA TO OCCUPATION

This section describes the processes applicable to all construction projects, whatever the chosen method of procurement.

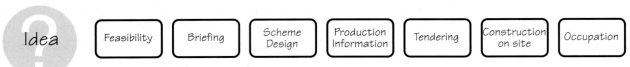

Idea | Feasibility | Briefing | Scheme Design | Production Information | Tendering | Construction on site | Occupation

THE PROCESSES

All projects go through the same basic processes, outlined in the diagram above.

The descriptions that follow place the key tasks in the context of a *designer-led* project. In other *procurement routes*, the processes are the same, but their sequence and responsibility for them will vary. In particular, *production information* and part or all of *scheme design* will be the responsibility of the *design and build organisation* in *design and build procurement*.

FEASIBILITY

THE NEED FOR FEASIBILITY STUDY

Before making any commitment to a project, the prudent *client* will carefully test that it is worthwhile by:

- clarifying the aims of the project
- checking that it is viable and that all the essential components are available and workable
- developing a strategy for implementation

After the initial appraisal the project may appear so straightforward that there seems little point in commissioning a formal study just to find out whether to go ahead. Why not just get on with it? However, if the project really is on the right lines, a quick *feasibility study* will demonstrate this, and everyone can proceed with greater confidence.

FIGURE 4.1   THE FEASIBILITY PROCESS

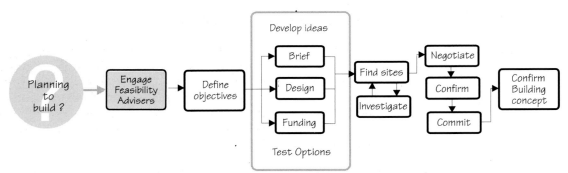

The feasibility study tests every aspect of the proposed project. Can the sort of building envisaged be provided within the constraints of the budget? Are there alternative ways of arranging the overall budget that would improve the opportunities and reduce the risks? Is more accommodation really necessary or could existing space be reorganised? Would this be cheaper? Is the intended site really suitable for this development? Is it likely to get planning permission? Are there hidden features, like bad ground conditions, lack of utilities, or insufficient space for future expansion that make it not viable?

It is surprising how often this process highlights opportunities or problems that might otherwise have been overlooked. Now is the best time to discover these and make any necessary changes to your plans.

INITIAL DESIGN OPTIONS

Initial design analysis is usually provided in the form of sketches which illustrate the various options for the project and the constraints that may be imposed by a particular site.

PRELIMINARY COST ESTIMATES

One of the first things to establish is the likely cost of the project and how it will be paid for. Once requirements for the project have been set down and discussed with *advisers*, it becomes possible to make preliminary estimates of the cost of the different elements. For the purpose of assessing your total liability these need to be examined under separate headings.

The **capital cost** will normally include:

- investigation of site or existing building(s)
- acquisition of land or buildings
- the building work
- any associated works e.g. site clearance, roads, drains, communication links etc
- fitting out the new building
- advisers' and other fees.

The **revenue budget** must make provision for:

- running costs (these will vary according to the standard of construction and equipment)
- cost of borrowing
- possible rental income.

Unavoidable 'one off' costs may be incurred such as:

- temporary adaptions
- relocation
- staged or phased occupation

INITIAL DEVELOPMENT OF THE BRIEF

At feasibility stage you will be required to start developing your *brief* to your advisers, by making choices and establishing priorities regarding the major issues, such as location, overall configuration of accommodation, or the relative importance of key facilities. These can then be tested against available sites and the budget to see what is practical. If this process is not conducted with thoroughness and honesty the project may fail.

FUNDING

Clarification of the budget and brief make it possible to initiate any borrowing that may be required. Potential lenders will need to know the value of the building on completion, its running costs and any potential income that could be derived from it.

The period of borrowing may have a critical impact on the way the project is managed. Your advisers will need to know the duration of the loan so that the approach adopted takes this into account.

TESTING AGAINST SITE CONSTRAINTS

As soon as the basic elements of the project begin to fit together and look promising it is essential to check out the key features about which the initial assumptions have been made. The most important of these is likely to be the site or existing building to be developed.

Lack of clarity early does not lead to the best solutions - the selection of wrong sites and 'make-do' arrangements

Making the right decisions early is more likely to give the right results later - suitable accommodation with appropriate facilities

The site will have its own constraints and these can shape the whole development of the project. They must be related to the budget and to the requirements for the building itself.

Firstly there are the conditions imposed by the local planning authority. These may determine:

- the type of building uses that are permitted
- any features, such as trees, that must be retained
- where a building can be placed on the site and its relation to adjoining properties
- the maximum allowable floor area for the development
- the height of any building and its appearance.

Physical site features also affect the design:

- contouring of the land
- shape of the plot
- context in relation to other buildings, roads, services etc.

If the site has been used previously, the existence of contaminated land or even the hidden remains of previous infrastructure can profoundly affect the viability of a project.

A key part of the feasibility study is to check the fundamental requirements of the brief against the site constraints. Only when it is clear that these are compatible can alternatives be explored and outline options developed.

SITE INVESTIGATIONS   At this stage definitive answers are not always available to all the questions. However, reasonable examination of site characteristics and available records should indicate any unusual conditions and the need for further detailed site investigations. In these circumstances a full geotechnical or other survey will prove a very worthwhile investment

Similarly while there is probably insufficient information to apply for full planning permission, initial enquiries normally make clear the likely requirements. It is extremely unwise to make a commitment to any major investment before you are satisfied that permission is likely to be forthcoming.

PLANNING PERMISSION   Achieving planning permission can take several months or more, and it must be one of the first things in the timetable if the project goes ahead. You have little control over planning delays, other than to see that your team responds swiftly to advice from the planning authority. Design and build organisations are very unlikely to guarantee their programme against planning difficulties. It is the client who carries the risk.

Obtaining planning permission is a legal pre-requisite to building, and its importance cannot be over-emphasised.

FEASIBILITY: CONCLUSIONS   No definite commitment should be made before you have received a full feasibility report setting out the main options. The report should indicate:

- cost
- planning or other legal constraints
- accommodation options, including any phasing
- the extent to which the brief is met
- timescales
- critical issues to be resolved
- alternative building procurement options
- next steps

This puts you in a position to decide whether to go ahead with briefing and *scheme design* or stop.

  | Feasibility | Briefing | Scheme Design | Production Information | Tendering | Construction on site | Occupation |

Idea

BRIEFING

BRIEF MAKING   Developing the brief is a collaborative and evolutionary process between client and advisers, that must be carefully and thoroughly undertaken. The project will meet your needs only if they are clearly identified and understood by your team.

Key aspects of the brief will be confirmed in the feasibility process, and the first task in implementing the project is to develop the details. These cover four main elements:

- A list of all activities that the building is to house; the relationship between each; the number of people involved; any special conditions or amenities that are required.

- The budget for all the components including the building, furnishings, other specialist works (like landscaping), all the design and other fees and costs and any critical timing related to these.

- A programme showing in outline all the stages of the design and construction work including the participants and key activities.

- The control procedures that are to be used to guide the progress of the project within the time and budget constraints. These need to include the methods of communication and authorisation as the works proceed.

Ask your advisers what information they need and when it is required. Be realistic about what you can achieve and don't be pressurised into providing inadequate information too quickly. The information that you provide at this stage lays the foundations for the future success of the project. No building can be better than its brief.

COMPLETING THE BRIEF

In a designer-led or other project where there is *multi-point* responsibility to the client, the brief can be refined as the design is developed. However if there is to be *single point* responsibility for design and construction, the brief must be firm and complete before the design and build organisation is appointed.

SCHEME DESIGN

The purpose of scheme design is to develop the project far enough for you to be sure that it will meet both your requirements and those of the planning authority, and any other body that needs to be consulted. Members of the team typically involved in a designer-led project and their activities are illustrated in Figure 4.2 The issues will be the same if a procurement route is being followed in which a design and build organisation has responsibility for total design, although the framework of responsibilities will be different.

FIGURE 4.2 RELATIONSHIPS DURING SCHEME DESIGN

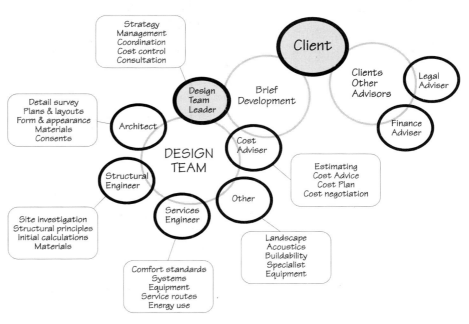

Although the broad shape of the brief should be defined and the budget established by the feasibility process, you may still have only a very general idea of what the scheme really 'looks like': there are still a great many decisions to be made.

The design development process is similar to the feasibility stage except that now there are a number of fixed points of reference. The aim is to increase these to the point where uncertainty has been largely eliminated. The work at this stage is mainly about defining the principles of the spatial arrangements, standards and construction methods. These are likely to undergo changes as the detail of the brief evolves and options are tested against the cost plan.

COST PLAN Understanding and controlling costs is a part of the continuing process of securing best value. At the start of scheme design, the *cost adviser* will draw up a *cost plan* with the *design team*. The building is broken down into separate elements (walls, floors, roof etc), each with an estimated cost reflecting the size and quality of the building envisaged.

Generally the costs used for the initial estimate are built up from previous experience of similar work. As the details of the project become more definite the costs are refined and revised. The cost plan is a positive tool and active throughout the design process. Its function is to enable the design team to explore the cost effect of various options with you.

At this stage the likely cost-in-use, that is the recurring costs of maintenance, heating, cleaning etc can also be taken into account. Techniques for building life-cycle costing have been developed and are available to the cost adviser.

At the end of scheme design you should receive a report including drawings and other information enabling you:

- to know the general arrangement and appearance of the proposed building
- to know how much it is likely to cost
- to make formal applications for consent to develop
- to authorise the start of the next stage.

SECHEME DESIGN: CONCLUSIONS

This is an important stage to reach and should be recorded by your formal acceptance of the design and agreement that no further changes should be made to it. All parties must accept that the design should be frozen at this point, although some details may need further clarification.

Idea — Feasibility — Briefing — Scheme Design — Production Information — Tendering — Construction on site — Occupation

PRODUCTION INFORMATION

The next part of the process takes the 'picture' of the building established during the scheme design stage and converts it into production information from which it can actually be built. The procurement strategy chosen will determine when and by whom this information is produced.

INFORMATION FRAMEWORK

The framework for this information is provided by the production drawings. These are supported by written *specifications* which define the materials and standards required. The specifications may be a separate document or form part of the *bills of quantities*, where these are used.

Specialist suppliers and subcontractors, such as those providing lifts, may undertake the detailed design of their own work themselves. Arrangements of this kind are increasingly common as sophisticated factory-made building components become more widely used. Where this occurs it is essential that the project arrangements are such that:

- the specialist can make a contribution to the design process when this is required
- the specialist design is coordinated with that of the design team

STATUTORY CONSENT

- design responsibility is clearly allocated (and paid for)

Design of specialist items can involve complex relationships in procurement methods with multipoint responsibility. It is a potential source of great difficulty, and must be carefully addressed in the contract documents and management arrangements.

In addition to requiring planning permission, buildings must comply with the *Building Regulations* and any other relevant legislation. The regulations cover a range of topics, mainly to do with health and safety; they also include requirements for such matters as energy conservation and access for people with disabilities. They set only minimum standards upon which you may well wish to improve.

Local authorities, or other administering bodies charge mandatory scale fees for handling these applications. These fees are additional to the fees you pay your advisers.

Approval under the Building Regulations is required before work starts on site. The construction work itself is subject to inspections to ensure compliance with the Building Regulations approval.

TIMESCALES Timescales required for the processes of design and construction vary, and every project will have its own critical events.

Some procurement options allow projects to be "*fast-tracked*" by overlapping processes that are strictly sequential in the traditional designer-led approach. Some broadly indicative timescales are illustrated in figure 4.3

FIGURE 4.3 APPROXIMATE TYPICAL TIMESCALES FOR A MEDIUM SIZED PROJECT

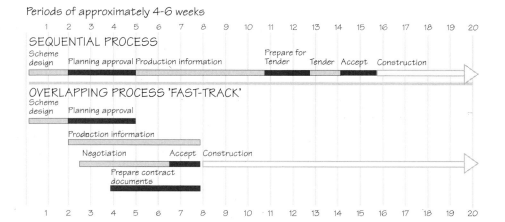

You should agree with your advisers a programme that not only recognizes your own objectives but also allows a realistic time for the designers to do their work. For instance, while it may appear that not much is going on during the production information phase, it is (or should be) a period of considerable activity. Assembling production information is a complex and time-consuming operation, involving the coordination and description of every component that will make up the finished building.

The temptation to reduce the period of time available for this part of the process should be resisted. If used productively it will provide a firm basis for a successful project on site. Enough time also needs to be allowed in the programme for you to check that the proposed building still complies with your brief, and that you are happy with the detailed specification that has been developed by the design team.

| Idea | Feasibility | Briefing | Scheme Design | Production Information | Tendering | Construction on site | Occupation |

TENDERING

BASIS OF TENDERING

The objective of tendering is to secure best value for money, not simply the lowest price for the construction work. This is normally achieved by inviting competitive tenders, although a single *negotiated tender* can be more appropriate in circumstances where:

- specialist skills or products of limited availability are required
- you have recently been through competitive tendering for similar work, and wish to use the same firm again. This can bring the advantage of building on a good working relationship.
- it is particularly important to secure the early involvement of the builder.

'Partnering' is a procedure increasingly used by experienced clients. It is founded upon an open and cooperative approach to the project, and demands considerable confidence on the part of the client. It usually, but not necessarily, implies longer term relationships, and does not exclude the principle of competition. Even those new to the industry should seek to establish the attitude of teamwork that is the hallmark of partnering.

OPEN AND SELECTIVE TENDERING

Competitive selection should be based on a balanced consideration of time, cost and quality. The weighting you give to these key criteria will depend on your objectives and the procurement route followed. For example:

- in designer-led procurement, if carefully pre-selected firms are invited to bid against a fully developed design and specified quality, price is likely to be the deciding factor
- if bids are invited from design and build organisations, the quality of design and specifications offered will be a major criterion in the final selection.

In all cases, the attitude of the firm, its reliability and quality of work must be carefully considered.

Competitive tendering should be selective rather than open, that is, restricted to a limited number of firms who have been pre-selected (or 'pre-qualified') to bid for the project. This has a number of advantages:

- only suitable firms are invited to bid
- those bidding know that they do so on an equal footing
- each has a reasonable chance of success
- the cost of tendering to the industry - and ultimately to its clients - is limited.

The 'Codes of Procedure' published by the industry's National Joint Consultative Council should always be observed. In particular, between

3 and 6 bids only should be sought on designer-led projects - no more than 3 should bid for design and build contracts.

Public bodies must comply with the UK regulations derived from EU Directives designed to promote competition.

PRESELECTION

Building firms potentially capable of carrying out the work can be identified from a number of sources, ranging from individual recommendation to advertisement in the local and construction press. Suitable firms are short-listed on the basis of criteria such as:

- their interest in the work and availability to carry it out.
- their previous experience of the type of work
- their recent performance
- their financial soundness

TENDER INFORMATION AND TIMESCALES

The documents used for tendering need not include every detail, but must contain enough information to enable the tenderers to price both the work itself and the risks involved - and to enable you to make sensible comparisons. Each tenderer must have the same information and the same opportunity to submit a tender by a fixed date and time.

Provisional sums may be included for items that cannot be priced by the tenderers, and which might be subject to later instructions. If the provisional sums amount to a significant proportion of the anticipated tender sum, they can distort the basis of tendering and imply that the tender documents are not adequately prepared.

The period for tendering must be adequate. The normal period is from four to six weeks, unless the tender involves a major element of design, when more time should be allowed.

TENDER OPENING AND ASSESSMENT

On opening tenders an initial assessment is made by the design team, or the *project manager*, to establish which should be analyzed in greater depth. Tenders are examined for both content and any major inconsistencies which could make them unworkable. Obvious errors are drawn to the attention of the tenderer who is usually given the opportunity either to stand by or withdraw his offer. For reasons of practical probity it is very unusual for a tender to be amended and accepted. In the case of a design and build offer, the evaluation process is more complex and may also include a presentation of the tender proposal. A forecast of expenditure in the form of a predicted monthly cashflow should be obtained from the tenderer.

CHANGES BEFORE CONTRACT

With good cost planning and control, tenders should be within budget, but at times of high inflation, or when the building industry is busy, this can be difficult to ensure. Where the lowest tender significantly exceeds the cost plan estimate, and fresh offers are unlikely to produce lower tenders, reducing either the scope or the specification of the project may be the only way to stay within budget. Despite the inconvenience of changes at this late stage, it is much better to make them before contractual commitment than hope they can be made when work is under way. They often can not and it is the client who will be faced with the bill.

PREPARATION BEFORE COMMITMENT

Before entering into a contract, it is sensible to make a final check of the project arrangements and the implications of this commitment. You need to be satisfied that you can meet the demands the contract will make. Is the site fully available? Have alternative arrangements been completed to provide facilities for those who may be displaced? Can the financial commitments be met? Have the appropriate insurances been taken out? What arrangements are to be made for the day-to-day supervision of the works?

The working arrangements for the contract are usually sorted out at a round-table meeting with all the parties concerned. This is the last opportunity to make sure that all the important issues are understood by everyone and are incorporated in the final contract documents.

It is particularly important that clear and simple procedures are in place to control changes to the contract after work has begun on site. Variations to the work originally envisaged in the contract can be costly and cause delay. You must have arrangements with your advisers to approve any such instructions before these are issued to the builder, based on an assessment of cost and other implications. The only exceptions should be on the grounds of clear practical necessity.

Remember that under most standard forms of contract the client is not empowered to give instructions direct to the builder.

?
Site start
check list

See Appendix 5 ⟩

Idea | Feasibility | Briefing | Scheme Design | Production Information | Tendering | Construction on site | Occupation

CONSTRUCTION ON SITE

Good programming by all concerned is a prerequisite of any successful project.

You should expect to receive a copy of the builder's programme. He will try to plan events so that critical tasks occur in the best sequence and in a way that provides each trade with as smooth a flow of work as possible. For this to happen it is essential that information, materials and labour are available when required. Even a relatively straightforward job can involve more than 20 separate trades. A more complex project may have many times this number. Delay or disruption to almost any one of these can have a serious effect upon the progress and cost of the project as a whole.

From the moment work starts on site, preparation has to be made for things that follow, sometimes many months later. For example holes for heating pipes or enclosures for lifts have to be accommodated in the basic structure long before they are actually installed. Late decisions which change these basic elements can be disruptive - and expensive. Some changes are unavoidable - equipment is no longer available or the actual construction of an existing building is found to be different from that envisaged. Such situations have to be overcome by everyone working together to find the most acceptable solution. Bear in mind that you may have to pay for changes if they are not the builder's responsibility.

CONTINGENCY PLANS As part of an overall strategy for managing risk in the project, you should have established a contingency sum for unforeseen additional costs. If it becomes apparent that this is likely to be inadequate, you must decide whether and at what point to seek savings. Ask your advisers to draw up a list of options. It is worth considering these very carefully in advance, so that a decision can be made quickly if cost problems do occur. The further a project has gone, the more difficult it is to take remedial action.

STANDARDS Builders work to the standards called for by the drawings and specifications. These usually refer to recognised industry standards which include British Standards and Codes of Practice. Manufacturers also supply technical information describing how and where their products should be used.

On designer-led projects the builder frequently agrees the standards of finish and workmanship with the design team, on the basis of samples, used as a reference for succeeding work. The *contract administrator* is responsible for ensuring that the standards specified are established on site and for periodic monitoring of the work. However, provision for day to day inspection must be made separately, normally by employing a *clerk of works* and/or other specialist *inspector*. Alternatively the design team appointments can be extended to include additional time on site for inspection. Technically complex projects may require resident architects and engineers. The design team can advise if this is necessary.

Materials such as concrete are routinely sampled and sent away to laboratories for strength and chemical testing. Work suspected to be substandard may be opened up for examination, and if found to be defective, rejected and done again at the builder's expense.

Under most of the standard forms of contract the clerk of works is strictly only an inspector with limited powers of instruction. In practice, he often plays a vital part in the smooth running of the contract by acting as a focus for communication. He sorts out the on-site problems with the relevant parties, as they occur, and makes sure that the builder understands any instructions he receives. The appointment of a good clerk of works is always a worthwhile investment.

MONITORING THE BUILDING CONTRACT Your advisers will hold regular meetings with the builder to discuss the progress of the job, information requirements, and so on. Attending these might be useful, but as they can be long and technical, it may be better to hold your own progress meetings with your immediate advisers and discuss only matters of particular interest to you.

The client automatically receives copies of all the instructions given to the builder. You cannot be expected to be aware of the implications of all of them but it is wise to keep generally abreast of what is going on. At your progress meetings you should ask for an explanation of anything that you do not fully understand.

Financial reports based on the regular valuations prepared by the cost adviser can provide a reasonable indication of progress, by charting the actual value of work done in comparison with the original cash flow forecast. A difference of more than 10% between the two figures is a reason for anxiety and question. The same financial reports can also give an early warning of any upward drift in the anticipated final cost. Make sure that information on current costs is up-to-date and as realistic as possible - however unwelcome this may sometimes be. Be ready with your advisers to implement the contingency plans if they are needed. Make sure that the builder is aware of them, and that the implications for his work programme have been fully taken into account. Contingency plans cannot be put into action without your authority.

DELAYS AND HOW THEY ARE DEALT WITH

If delays do occur, it is important to be aware of their implications as soon as possible. Most of the standard forms of contract include time as a key element and have arrangements for apportioning responsibility for delay and therefore who pays for its effects. Reasons for delay can be broadly categorized:

- builder's responsibility
- client's or his advisers' or agents' responsibility
- 'neutral' events outside the control of either party

If the builder is responsible he may be required to compensate the client for any losses suffered as a direct result of the delay. The rate of such recovery may be included in the contract as *Liquidated and Ascertained Damages (LADs)*. These are calculated when the contract details are drawn up, as a genuine pre-estimate of the cost of delay to the client.

It is important to be aware that this is your only remedy, under the contract, for the effects of delay and therefore the amount needs to be carefully considered. You will be entitled to deduct from sums owed to the builder the LADs for any period of time by which the project over-runs the contract completion date (taking into account any *extensions of time*). The period ends on the date on which the building is certified by the contract administrator as being *practically complete*.

The other side of this coin is that the standard forms of contract also provide for the builder to be relieved of the effects of LADs if he can demonstrate that he did not cause the delay. In these circumstances the builder makes a request for an extension of time to the contract period equivalent to the delay he considers that he has suffered. If his request is accepted by the contract administrator then an *extended contract completion* date is set.

When the builder prices his tender he makes allowances for the cost of site huts, scaffolding, management, site supervision and so on. If the contract over runs he may pay for these items for longer than he had anticipated. He is entitled to recover theses costs if he can demonstrate that the delay was caused by the client or his advisers. He may also be entitled to recover the cost of any disruption and other losses sustained as a direct consequence of these or other factors in the client's control.

The standard forms of contract give the ground rules for these procedures, typically setting out:

- the circumstances in which the builder is compensated
- how liability is apportioned if the contract is affected by neutral events
- who is responsible for awarding extensions of time to the builder and apportioning liability for the cost of delays or disruption (most frequently the contract administrator with the cost adviser).

The process of settling *builder's claims* can be very complex and time consuming. Moreover, delay in reaching a sensible outcome can seriously affect the spirit in which the contract is conducted. Failure to reach agreement can lead to external arbitration or even full legal proceedings.

Your advisers have a duty to keep you fully aware of the progress of any outstanding claims. You should insist on being kept up to date and be prepared to accept a well supported case for settlement. If you believe that your advisers have caused delay or disruption by giving bad or late advice your redress is against them and not against the builder.

| Idea | Feasibility | Briefing | Scheme Design | Production Information | Tendering | Construction on site | Occupation |

COMPLETION

OCCUPATION

Your building should be finished by the original or extended contract completion date. However, finishing a building is always difficult - many activities have to be coordinated and completed at the same time. Builders invariably tend to be optimistic about what they can achieve. Your advisers should keep you informed as to when *handover* is likely to take place. Seek a realistic assessment, as you will have your own arrangements to make before taking possession.

It is often helpful to inspect the work with your advisers some time before it is offered for handover. If you identify any changes required before the building can be used, you must consider your options very carefully:

- if the builder confirms that the work can be undertaken at reasonable cost and without causing delay, he might be instructed to carry it out

- if the work is at all likely to be disruptive you may be exposing yourself to costly claims. In such cases, it is wise to complete the first contract and set up a further, separate contract for the alterations.

Practical completion is an important stage contractually. It marks the end of the builder's possession and free access to the site and fixes the date from which any contractual time-related events are calculated.

The formality of handover can only be achieved when a building has reached this stage and is certified as practically complete.

Frequently there is pressure on both the client and builder to achieve completion - and occupation - as soon as possible. Ideally everything should be absolutely finished when the building is handed over, but this is seldom the case and in reality most clients agree to accept handover with some minor items incomplete. Before agreeing to this you should be satisfied that the outstanding items are genuinely minor and will not affect your use of the building. They must be fully recorded and arrangements made for the builder to deal with them within an

TAKEOVER   agreed period.

Taking over a building is not unlike to buying a new car. Buildings, like cars, need looking after. They need maintenance, regular servicing, insurance and good management to keep them fully useable.

At handover the client should be given a 'manual' for the building. This is compiled by his advisers and should include:

- a description of the building, usually including 'as-built' drawings
- information on the materials and components used, including their care and maintenance
- technical specifications and operating instructions for equipment such as boilers, lifts and security systems.

You should also receive copies of all certificates of compliance, warranties or guarantees obtained as part of the design and construction process.

MANAGING YOUR BUILDING   Check carefully what these cover, and any conditions attached to them.

The future management of the building needs to be considered well in advance of taking it over. How is the regular maintenance to be carried out? What equipment needs to be serviced? Who will be responsible for the building control systems ? There will be many other such questions which have to be answered. One option is to appoint a *facilities manager* who can take responsibility for all the equipment and systems, and the building fabric. Another is to set up service contracts with separate specialist firms. Whatever you decide to do, the arrangements must be in place and preparatory training completed by the time the building is

DEALING WITH DEFECTS   handed over.

The builder is responsible for putting right any *latent defects* for a specified period of time after practical completion. This is known as the '*defects liability period*' and usually lasts for a year. Most new buildings take time to settle down and a few problems can be expected. The most common defects result from shrinkage or minor movement and require adjustment and touching up to the decorations. You may consider that something is not working properly. This may - or may not - be the fault of the builder. If in doubt discuss the problem with your advisers first. When problems occur they should be reported by the contract administrator to the builder immediately. Problems that are urgent should be dealt with at once and only minor items left till later. When reporting defects you should provide as much information as possible so that the person who comes to rectify them knows what to expect and brings the right equipment. You should also keep records of all your complaints so that both you and the contract administrator are aware of what has gone wrong.

The heating and other building services should have been fully commissioned and in full working order at handover. It is likely though, that some adjustments will continue to be necessary for a while. Make sure that you know who is responsible for these and for how long.

On the expiry of the defects liability period the building is thoroughly inspected by all parties to the contract and the builder arranges to carry out any outstanding remedial work. Upon satisfactory completion the building can be certified as complete. The builder retains liability for defects that become apparent in the future. This liability is normally effective for a period of six years after practical completion for contracts 'under hand', or for twelve years if the contract was executed as a deed. Redress under common law may extend to 15 or 16 years after completion.

THE FINAL ACCOUNT

Latent defects insurance is available, but must be arranged at the outset of the project. You should seek specific advice.

Once the main construction activity is over, work continues on settling the accounts for the building work. The ease and speed with which this is done depends upon the type of contract used and any changes that have occurred since the original contract was made. The process can be completed in a few weeks or take many months, depending upon the circumstances. The *final account* brings together all the financial issues relating to the contract and includes the settlement of any claims made by the builder. The final resolution of these may require protracted negotiation. The issue of the *final certificate* has the effect of closing the right of either party to make further claims under the contract except in relation to defects.

SECTION 5
CHOICES - THE CRITERIA

This section identifies some of the key issues that need to be considered in making the choice about the most appropriate procurement route for your project.

CHOOSING THE ROUTE

There are many routes to procuring building work. Each differs in the way the necessary skills and services are assembled and organised. They allocate risks and responsibilities in various ways, and offer different advantages and disadvantages to the client. No single option can meet all possible *client* objectives. For example:

- time, cost and quality will always be in tension. Usually an improvement in one can only be achieved at the cost of another
- the ability to control the project involves taking responsibility for risk. The more control the client wishes to have, the more risk he should expect to bear.

Like politics, building *procurement* is an 'art of the possible'. The trick is to find the best balance, by defining very clearly your objectives and priorities, and matching these against the demands and advantages of the various procurement options. The key considerations are:

- timing
- cost
- quality
- flexibility
- risk
- responsibility

TIMING   The nature of the building work itself will be an influence.

This section of the guide poses key questions to be asked, and provides some pointers to the answers. The next section outlines the procurement options in most common use

Every project has its own critical time requirements. You need to consider which aspects are important to you.

Must a building contract be in place by a particular date?

If an early start to construction is essential you will have to chose an arrangement that shortens the precontract period and allows some design and other preparatory work to be done after the building contract is signed.

Is it primarily the construction period that you wish to time limit?

This may be a requirement if the total financial package is dependent upon borrowing or quick returns from sale or rental. It is likely to be important where work will be carried out to an occupied building. It implies an arrangement in which time is invested in survey, design and other preparatory work, prior to commitment to the construction contract

Must the building be in use by an early, specific date?

This points to a procurement route that provides overall speed, for example by over-lapping design and construction.

Is time really not important?

If time is relatively unimportant, exploit this to achieve other priorities.

Generally, there are a number of responses to time constraints, all of which have implications for procurement strategy, and which have to be weighed against other priorities. They include:

- designing the building so that it uses prefabrication or other fast construction methods
- creating enabling contracts, such as early demolition, to bring forward or reduce subsequent construction time
- overlapping activities that are usually carried out sequentially
- starting critical parts of the work before all decisions are made
- phasing to allow early completion of critical accommodation

COST Cost and the management of cash flow are major considerations in many projects. They have a profound effect on the nature and management of the procurement process.

Is the funding for the total project subject to a strict cash limit?

This will demand procedures that allow control of all elements of the process: design and other advisory services, fitting out and occupation, and any other commitments, as well as of construction work. The construction contract itself should offer high price certainty. An absolute cash limit will severely limit options in other respects.

Do you need an absolutely firm price for construction prior to signing the contract?

This is nominally achievable under several procurement arrangements, depending on the form of contract used. It demands careful consideration of the risks, where they lie, and how they are priced.

How important are future running costs?

The cost of constructing a building can be small compared with the total cost of occupying it for a number of years. If maintenance, security, heating, lighting and other running costs are significant, the procurement arrangement must give the client considerable control over design and specification.

How available is funding and are there particular requirements attached to authorization or timing?

If funding is time-limited or requires certain undertakings to be completed before it is made available, this must be recognised in the procurement arrangements. Remember that once you enter into a contract you must have funds available to match your contractual obligations.

Your fundamental objective should be to secure best value for money in relation to the total cost of the project, rather than simply the lowest cost of advice or construction. Whatever your procurement strategy, those working for you should follow a disciplined approach to *value management*, which is covered by a separate CIRIA guide. The way the project is managed will always have a direct effect on ultimate cost; you must pay particular attention to:

- availability when required of your own resources and those of your advisers, and efficiency of their deployment.
- clarity and firmness of the *brief*
- precision and availability of information to your *advisers* and to the *builder*

QUALITY Appropriate design and workmanlike construction is achievable through any of the normal building processes. Rapid construction or a limited budget need not imply a quality that is inadequate for the clients needs, provided these are clearly expressed at the start. However, if there are specific requirements for particular quality, they will demand careful consideration of procurement procedure.

How important is the appearance of your building to you or your organisation?

You may want your building to present a particular image of your organisation. This may require the use of expensive materials or a building with distinctive architecture. This implies a procurement arrangement that gives you a close relationship with the designers.

How important is the reliability of your building?

If your building is to house equipment or activities which require special conditions that must be maintained with exceptional reliability, the relevant specialist designers and installers will have a critical role. The procurement arrangement should acknowledge this, and probably give you a direct relationship with them.

However much care is invested in design and specification, the quality of the final product depends on whether the standards specified are achieved. Unlike many manufacturers the building industry is primarily involved in assembling one-off products and frequently does this under extremely adverse physical conditions. Good and constant quality management and control is essential even for the simplest buildings, with an appropriate level of supervision, and inspection. Whatever the procurement approach, firms working on the project should be able to demonstrate that they can manage the quality of their own work; effective operation of a *quality management* system is a good indicator.

FLEXIBILITY Ideally a client's requirements are clarified and fixed in a comprehensive brief before extensive detail design is undertaken, and particularly before a contract is placed for construction. However circumstances do not always permit this, and in such cases the project strategy must be very carefully considered to avoid disruption and abortive costs.

Do you anticipate the need to revise or finalise your requirements during the course of the project?

Some procurement arrangements allow the client to keep options open longer than others. However, such flexibility, will be limited, and it may be better to plan for phased contracts.

How much flexibility is necessary in the building itself to cope with possible future change?

This requirement, like any client need, will be incorporated in the brief, and is a matter of design. The designers will exercise their skill whatever the procurement arrangement, but depending on the complexity of the building it may be preferable for them to have a direct relationship with the client.

RISK No construction project is risk free. The client, builder and other parties to a project accept different degrees of risk under the various procurement arrangements. The client should decide how much risk to accept and plan procurement strategy accordingly.

Do you wish to transfer all construction risk to the builder?

Between them the different procurement routes and forms of contract offer a wide range of possibilities for transferring risk to the builder. This is not a simple decision to take: you will need advice. Remember the builder will wish to price for the risk he takes. Other methods of managing the risk may be more effective.

How much of the design risk do you wish to retain?

Responsibility for design can be a complex issue. Its nature and allocation depends on the procurement route and the terms of the contracts and agreements. Design and build can offer the client the opportunity to transfer more of the design risk than other approaches.

Whatever procurement route is followed, the client should adopt a disciplined and systematic approach to *risk management*. This is emerging as a discipline in its own right, and is the subject of a separate CIRIA guide.

RESPONSIBILITY The various procurement systems involve different relationships and responsibilities for the client; these make a wide range of demands upon him and his organisation.

What role will you and your organisation play? How much of the management of the project will your experience, technical capability and resources enable you to take an?

If your capability and resources are limited, you will avoid procurement arrangements that make heavy demands directly on the client. Better options could include delegation to a *project manager*, or a procurement arrangement that allows maximum support from advisers.

Do you want responsibility for the project to be concentrated in as few points as possible, or are you happy for different aspects to be separately managed by a number of people directly responsible to you?

Both extremes are possible under different procurement arrangements.

How much control do you wish to exercise over the project or specific aspects of it?

If you require to be closely involved with development of the design, you must choose a procurement route that gives you a direct relationships with the designers. If you wish to have control over any aspect of the construction work, this must be anticipated in your contractual relationship with the builder. Remember that the more control you wish to have, the more risk and responsibility you must be willing to bear.

THE NATURE OF THE PROJECT

The nature of the construction work you are proposing to undertake will have a profound effect on the way you tackle the project. It will be reflected in all the considerations listed above in this section, and could itself point clearly to particular procurement options.

Is the building work essentially straightforward, or is it complex, technically difficult, or subject to particular risks ?

The best approach to the project will be quite different if, for example, your requirement is for a simple warehouse, for refurbishing an historic building, or for premises to house highly sensitive equipment.

MAKING THE DECISION

PROCUREMENT ROUTE

There is no simple, mechanistic system for choosing the best procurement route. For many projects there will be more than one realistic option. You may find it helpful to list the various procurement arrangements, which are outlined in the next section, and score them against your priorities. You should always seek expert and completely objective advice before committing to a particular procurement stratgey.

FORMS OF CONTRACT

Many of the procurement arrangements are supported by standard forms of contract for the building work, including some recently published. Their respective merits and problems are debated at length in the industry. Selection of an appropriate form of contract can follow after the basic procurement strategy is in place, again with reference to your objectives and priorities. You will need careful and detailed advice from your project advisers, particularly if you are contemplating altering standard forms, or drafting a bespoke contract.

?
Standard
contracts

See appendix 7 ▷

**ABOVE ALL......
TEAMWORK**

While appropriate procurement arrangements are vitally important, it is even more important that those you appoint to work on the project have the skills to undertake the job, and work well together and with you. If you achieve this, it is the best possible basis for a successful project.

SECTION 6
CHOICES - THE OPTIONS

This section sets out the principle procurement options. It describes the main arrangements and characteristics of each, including their advantages and disadvantages.

OVERVIEW

The choice of building procurement systems is widely varied. A key defining feature is the way in which responsibility is allocated by the *client*. This guide distinguishes between:

- *Multipoint* systems, in which a number of organisations are separately responsible for design and construction
- *Single point* systems, in which a single organisation takes complete or substantial responsibility for both design and construction.

A further key distinguishing feature is the way the organisation responsible to the client for construction is paid. This can be on the basis of a:

- *Lump sum*, based on figures quoted in the tender for carrying out the construction work
- *Management fee* for directing and coordinating the construction work.

Descriptions of the procedures most commonly used and their main variants follow in this section. For the sake of clarity, roles and relationships are described without reference to a *project manager* acting on behalf of the client.

Standard contracts

See appendix 7

[DESIGNER-LED]

DESIGNER-LED MULTIPOINT PROCEDURE

KEY FEATURES   *Designer-led* procurement with multipoint responsibility to the client is usually referred to as the *'traditional'* approach and is still the most commonly used system in the UK.

FIGURE 6.1   DESIGNER-LED MULTIPOINT PROCUREMENT: ORGANISATIONAL RELATIONSHIPS

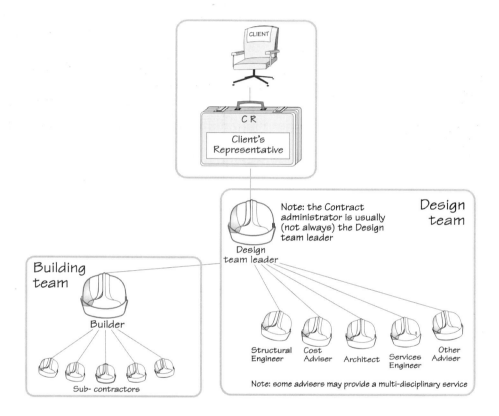

Its key features are:

- the *design team leader* acts as principal adviser and usually agent of the client on all aspects of the project throughout its life
- the *design team* provides all design and other information upon which *builders'* tenders are obtained
- the builder contracts with the client to carry out construction to the design and standards prescribed by the design team.

Organisational relationships do not necessarily reflect contractual relationships. The design team leader has a 'supervisory' role for the work of both the design team and the builder (Figure 6.1), even though the contractual responsibilities of the various parties (Figure 6.2), lie directly with the client (*employer*).

[DESIGNER-LED]

FIGURE 6.2   DESIGNER-LED MULTIPOINT PROCUREMENT: CONTRACTUAL RELATIONSHIPS

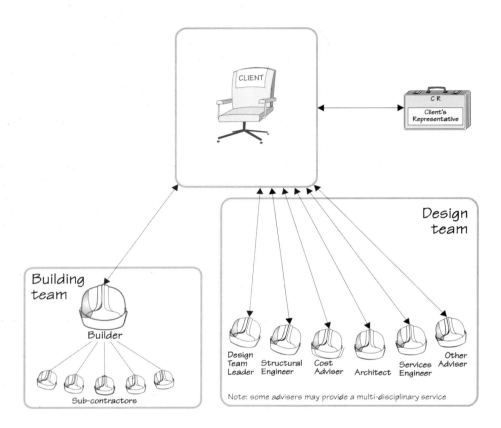

ROLES
THE CLIENT

The terms on which you appoint your design team determine the nature and extent of your day to day involvement in the project, particularly during the precontract stages. Once construction work starts, client contact with the builder is restricted; most standard contracts require all communications to be channelled through the *contract administrator* (usually the design team leader).

You can chose either to appoint the separate disciplines of the design team individually, (*architects, engineers, cost adviser* etc) or collectively under a single appointment. There are advantages and disadvantages for each method. Separate appointments imply a more direct relationship with the client whereas a collective appointment focuses responsibility on the design team leader. Cost advisers often say that a direct contractual relationship with the client reinforces the independence of their advice, even though they are still full members of the design team. Whichever arrangement is adopted the design team leader is responsible for co-ordinating the work of the rest of the team. The terms of agreement need to make this clear.

THE DESIGN TEAM

The team usually starts small - just the design team leader and the cost adviser - and builds up as the project develops. Specialist skills are added, with the client's agreement, as and when they are required.

[DESIGNER-LED]

This design team normally undertakes to:

- provide all the services necessary to develop the *brief* and design for the approval of the client
- obtain all necessary statutory consents
- coordinate and provide all *production information*
- draw up a *specification* for materials and workmanship
- advise on suitable builders and obtain tenders
- administer the contract
- agree the *final account* for settlement by the client
- provide cost information and advice throughout the project.

THE BUILDER   The builder is responsible for managing the construction process on site to the specified quality and to the agreed programme. This includes the performance of his subcontractors. (There are exceptions in the case of subcontractors nominated under certain standard forms of contract; you should discuss the implications with your *advisers*).

The builder is required to build the work to the design provided by the design team. He normally carries no responsibility for design except where this is specified in the contract. Where specialist suppliers or subcontractors are required to provide design expertise for their own work, separate *collateral warranties* should be set up to indemnify the client.

The diagrams at Figures 6.3 & 6.4 show how the builder's involvement relates to the design and construction process under *single* and *two stage tendering* arrangements.

TENDERING
SINGLE STAGE   In single stage tendering design and construction follow sequentially (Figure 6.3). Enough time must be allowed for the *scheme design* and production information stages to be completed before tenders are invited.

FIGURE 6.3   SEQUENCE:DESIGNER LED MULTIPOINT PROCUREMENT, SINGLE STAGE TENDERING

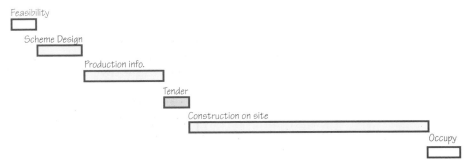

TWO STAGE   A two-stage tendering procedure permits the earlier involvement of the builder, for example if particular construction systems are on offer that have implications for the design. Tenders are invited on outline information (Figure 6.4) and firm prices negotiated with the selected

[DESIGNER-LED]

builder as production information is completed. A full contract is then entered into and proceeds as in the single-stage procedure.

FIGURE 6.4   SEQUENCE: DESIGNER- LED MULTIPOINT PROCUREMENT, TWO STAGE TENDERING

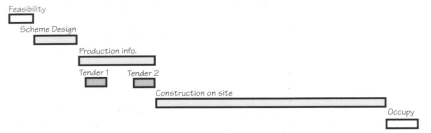

By overlapping some of the time normally allowed for tendering with the later part of the production information stage, the overall pre-start programme can be slightly reduced. However, if the process of agreeing the second-stage tender becomes protracted this time advantage can be lost. It is important to have all contract details agreed before the builder starts on site.

BASIS OF PAYMENT TO THE BUILDER

Various forms of contract allow different bases of payment to the builder. These have implications for clarity of final cost, and of risk accepted by the client

LUMP SUM

The builder offers to carry out the work for a *lump sum* based upon a full description of the work required. This arrangement implies very limited scope for change. However in practice the documentation used, which often includes *bills of quantities*, does allow for changes, with appropriate adjustment to the price. Lump sum tendering works well only if the work can be fully described and there are no significant changes during the course of the contract.

MEASURED

The builder prices the work on the basis of less accurate information which is subject to remeasurement when all the uncertainties have been eliminated. Tenders should include a schedule of rates to make pricing easier. Good cost planning and control are particularly important to ensure that the project stays within budget.

This arrangement is useful where it is essential to make an early site start before all the detailed production information is available, or where the full scope of the work, say to an existing building, cannot be established until it is opened up.

COST REIMBURSEMENT

The builder agrees to undertake work which cannot be accurately described, either by type or quantity, at the time when the tender documents are prepared. He tenders on the basis that he recovers the actual costs of labour, materials and equipment, and in addition is paid a fee to cover his management costs and profit.

In these circumstances the tender documents describe the broad scope of the work for which the builder tenders his management fee. The fee

[DESIGNER-LED]

may be fixed, fluctuating or on a sliding scale, depending on the actual value of the work.

This arrangement implies an inherent lack of price and time certainty and is usually only adopted if other options are not available because of the nature of the work or an over-riding need for speed.

ALLOWANCE FOR INFLATION

Tender rates are usually fixed for contract periods of two years or less. For longer contracts a fluctuating price basis may be adopted to allow for inflation.

CONTROL SYSTEMS

COST

The design team leader normally has overall responsibility for managing the cost of the project and keeping the client fully informed of any changes. After the contract has been signed with the builder this responsibility passes to the contract administrator. Monthly cost reports are drawn up by the cost adviser in consultation with the rest of the design team.

The contract administrator instructs the builder to carry out any necessary variations to the work. It is his duty to make sure that the client is aware of the implications of any variations, and that agreed procedures are followed regarding prior approval.

QUALITY

The design team leader also has overall responsibility for quality control. This includes the performance of his own design team as well as specifying the standard of building work. A *clerk of works* or other specialist *inspector* is often appointed to provide day- to- day on-site inspection. The design team leader advises when this will be necessary.

The builder is responsible for achieving the required standard of construction. The contract administrator may require work that does not meet the contract specification to be redone at the builder's expense. Work which is done correctly, but about which you, as client, are for some reason not happy, should be discussed first with the contract administrator, not the builder. If you want such work redone, you must pay for it.

ADVANTAGES AND DISADVANTAGES

The designer-led approach can offer the following benefits:

- you choose your own advisers to design and supervise the project, and maintain a close relationship with them
- the process is well understood by designers and builders alike
- commitment to spend large sums of money under the construction contract comes at a relatively late stage in the project
- tendering on substantially complete design information gives good indication of final construction cost before contractual commitment to the builder.

Potential disadvantages include:

- the sequential procedure cannot readily be compressed; other options allowing overlap may offer better overall speed.

[DESIGNER-LED]

- difficulties can arise if design information is not as firm and complete as anticipated in the contract
- separation of responsibility for design and construction can hinder a teamwork approach, and lead to adversarial attitudes if problems occur.
- late involvement of the builder can limit his contribution, for example in improving *buildability* of the design
- it can be difficult to integrate the contribution of specialist suppliers or installers, and complex projects can be difficult to manage.

SUPPORTING CONTRACT DOCUMENTATION

Standard documents exist to suit a wide range of jobs. It is very important that the most appropriate contract is used. The design team leader and/ or cost adviser will normally offer a recommendation.

MANAGEMENT CONTRACTING

KEY FEATURES

Management contracting was adopted in the UK in the early 1970s, particularly to meet the needs of large, complex or '*fast-track*' projects. An underlying philosophy was to enable the builder to work on the client's behalf on a more 'professional' basis, through reimbursement on a fee basis to remove conflicts of commercial interest. It is an arrangement with multipoint responsibility to the client. In principle, organisational and contractual relationships are similar to those in the traditional designer-led procedure (Figures 6.5 and 6.6). Under this arrangement the builder is known as the management contractor.

FIGURE 6.5   MANAGEMENT CONTRACTING - ORGANISATIONAL RELATIONSHIPS

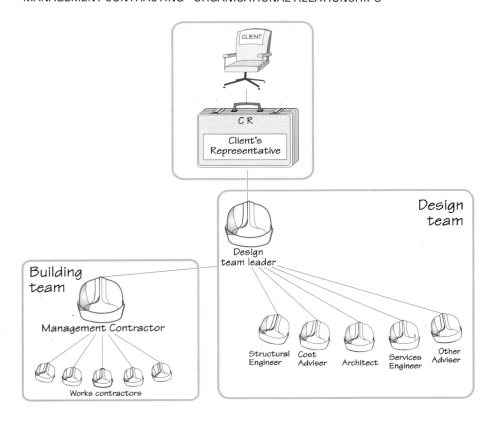

[MANAGEMENT CONTRACTING]

The main features of management contracting are:

- the management contractor tenders his services to manage the building process and also to work with the design team, helping on project planning and advising an construction methods.
- accordingly the appointment is made early, usually before scheme design stage has been completed
- the management contractor does not employ his own operatives on construction work. Rather it is divided into relatively self contained packages, tendered and carried out by *works contractors*, individually subcontracted to the management contractor
- as a result, construction is able to start before design is complete (for example, foundations may be put in before details of what goes on top are finally known - see Figure 6.7)
- the client reimburses the management contractor for work completed by the works contractors. Although he may be entitled to a small management charge ('discount') on the works contracts he does not receive any share of the profit on them.

The success of management contracting depends on the commitment of all parties to work together as a team. It requires:

- the management contractor to bring to the project proven and appropriate management skills and experience
- the client to take an active part in the project, and share risks as well as benefits

FIGURE 6.6   MANAGEMENT CONTRACTING - CONTRACTUAL RELATIONSHIPS

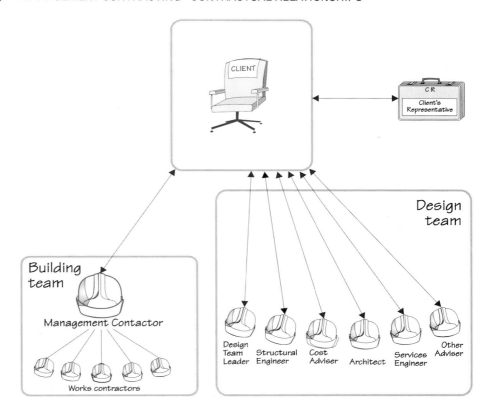

[MANAGEMENT CONTRACTING]

ROLES
THE CLIENT

Management contracting requires fast decision making - and quick responses from the client. It is important to be prepared for this. All those taking part must have enough experience to reach decisions and and to act quickly, and be prepared to work together. In these circumstances many clients appoint an in-house project manager.

Although the lines of responsibility for management contracting are similar to the traditional designer-led arrangement, it can make heavier demands on the client. These include:

- the need for more experienced personnel
- agreeing and authorising the work stages in more complex circumstances
- design decisions being run in parallel with the tendering for the initial works contracts.
- managing the project's funding against a less certain cost outcome

THE DESIGN TEAM

The design team has a very similar role to that under designer-led contract arrangements. The project begins with the core design team developing the brief and the initial scheme proposals. These form the basis for tenders by prospective management contractors.

The design team leader remains responsible for the administration of the contract, which includes setting standards, giving instructions and certifying payments for work done. He works closely with the management contractor during both the design and construction stages.

THE BUILDER

The management contractor's role is broader than under more traditional systems. He is responsible for:

- providing construction advice during scheme design
- overall construction programming and administration
- recommending and organising the works contractors including tendering
- managing and supervising work on site
- paying the works contractors
- ensuring that the actual building work is done efficiently and economically

The management contractor does not employ any labour directly other than that necessary for management and supervision of the works contractors and for welfare and 'attendance' arrangements.

TENDERING

The management contractor is normally selected on the basis of a detailed proposal:

- quoting a management fee
- describing the intended approach to the project
- naming the staff involved

Selection may be in two stages, with prequalification on the basis of an outline bid prior to full tendering. Final selection procedures always involve a full presentation and interview, involving key members of the prospective teams. Because of the time and effort involved, numbers invited to submit a full bid should be very limited.

Work packages are usually tendered competitively by the management contractor.

[MANAGEMENT CONTRACTING]

FIGURE 6.7   SEQUENCE: MANAGING CONTRACTING

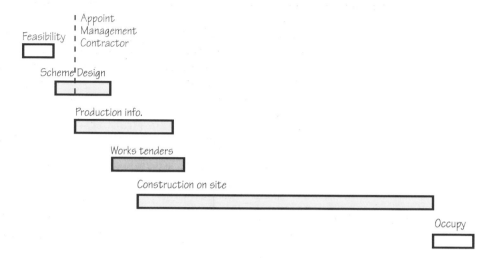

FEES AND CONSTRUCTION COSTS

Payments to the management contractor consist of two elements:

- fees
- reimbursable costs

The fee is based upon the initial *cost plan* and covers the builder's management services. When the cost plan estimate is agreed, the fee may be converted to a fixed sum, thus providing some performance incentive. The contract must define clearly what services are included in the fee and which are reimbursable.

Fees are generally between two and four per cent of the construction costs. The level agreed should take account of the potential savings that the management contractor expects to bring to the contract in his initial proposal. It is normal to divide the fee between pre-construction and construction periods, so that fee settlement is easier if the project does not go ahead.

Reimbursable costs normally include:

- all operatives directly employed by the management contractor on site, site facilities such as canteen and plant, cranes, scaffolding etc (where not covered by the works contracts). These may be consolidated into a lump sum

- the payments made by the management contractor to the works contractors. It is important that the management contractor is not tempted to earn interest by deliberately delaying payments

Because there is no contractual certainty about the final outcome of the work or costs, management contracting relies heavily for its cost control upon the regular updating and monitoring of the cost plan.

[MANAGEMENT CONTRACTING]

In order to provide a firm basis for overall cost control it is good practice to aim to let at least 60% of the total works contracts' value before construction starts.

Some forms of contract offered incorporate a *'target cost'* as a fundamental requirement. Where this is the case the management contractor's fee is geared, on a sliding scale, to the actual cost of construction. As a further incentive, a proportion of any savings greater than an agreed amount is taken by the management contractor. Alternatives of this kind should be discussed at the outset of the project.

The lack of firm prices at the start combined with the need to retain design flexibility makes it particularly important that projects using management contracting include a realistic contingency provision.

QUALITY

As with more traditional designer-led arrangements, the builder is responsible for making sure that the standards set by the design team are achieved.

ADVANTAGES AND DISADVANTAGES

Management contracting offers:

- the opportunity to reduce overall project timescales by overlapping design and construction
- the opportunity to set up a strong management team able to deal with complex or difficult projects
- some flexibility for change or late decisions where work packages have not been tendered
- potential overall cost benefits achieved by
  - improved buildability
  - work packages individually competitively tendered
  - phased completion to suit letting/occupation needs.

However, management contracting can increase the client's exposure to risk. In particular, final cost can be subject to greater uncertainty because:

- there is normally no overall contractual commitment to cost of construction until all the packages are let
- although works contractors are subcontracted to the management contractor, the client takes the ultimate risk of individual works contractors' insolvency
- cost increases which are caused by delay outside the control of the construction team are borne by the client
- commitment to the construction process is made before the design process is complete.

?
Standard
contracts

See appendix 7

SUPPORTING CONTRACT DOCUMENTATION

Management contracting relies heavily on both client and management contractor bringing to the project the necessary skill, commitment and attitudes. It requires a non-adversarial approach by all parties; without cooperation, complex contractual problems can arise.

Management contracting is now supported by standard documentation. A variety of non-standard contracts are also available from those who offer the service. These require careful scrutiny and it is wise to seek professional advice.

[CONSTRUCTION MANAGEMENT]

FIGURE 6.8   CONSTRUCTION MANAGEMENT - ORGANISATIONAL RELATIONSHIPS

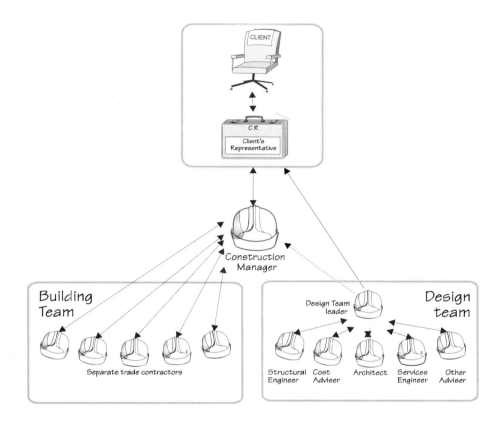

CONSTRUCTION MANAGEMENT

KEY FEATURES   *Construction management* is a development of management contracting that has been more recently applied in the UK. Organisations offering the service are known as '*construction managers*'. It is less clearly defined and documented then management contracting, but shares a key characteristic in that it is a service provided for a fee to manage the construction process. Other similarities to management contracting are:

- the construction manager is appointed at an early stage in the development of the project
- the construction works are divided into packages which are tendered and let to *trade contractors*
- it is possible to start work on site before design work is complete on all packages
- the design team are appointed by the client, in a multipoint framework of responsibility to the client.

However, there are key differences from management contracting:

- contracts for the works packages are made directly between the client and trade contractors; the client is responsible for making payments as advised by the construction manager

[CONSTRUCTION MANAGEMENT]

- although the construction manager is responsible for coordinating and directing the trade contractors, he carries no contractual liability for their work.

While management contracting is a service offered by major builders with a substantial capital base, construction management is offered by organisations from a wider range of size and background.

FIGURE 6.9   CONSTRUCTION MANAGEMENT - CONTRACTUAL RELATIONSHIPS

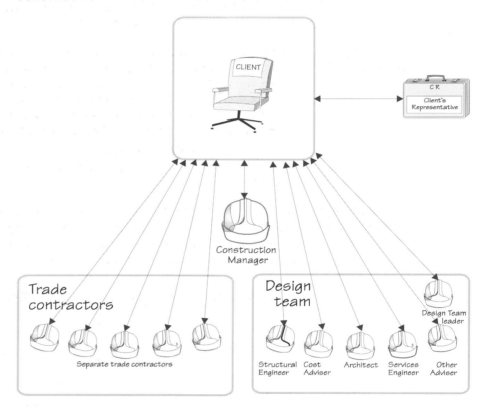

ROLES
THE CLIENT

Construction management places the client in a central position contractually (see Figures 6.8 and 6.9) and implies a high level of client involvement. The extent to which control is exercised by the client depends upon the level of delegation to the construction manager. This can be extensive but will never be complete.

Construction management is really suitable only if you or your representative are experienced and willing to take part fully in the construction process.

THE CONSTRUCTION
MANAGER

As part of his overall management and coordinating role, the construction manager will arrange and supervise the trade contracts on the client's behalf.

His terms of employment may include personal targets relating to time, cost and quality. He is required to carry out his duties with skill and care, and aim to meet the project's targets but not to guarantee its success. He is not responsible for the performance of other advisers or individual trade contractors.

[CONSTRUCTION MANAGEMENT]

The construction managers role may be broader than that of the management contractor, in particular to coordinate the design process. It may be extended to include other work normally undertaken by the client's advisers.

THE TRADE CONTRACTORS

Each trade contractor has a direct responsibility to the client and is expected to bear the cost of any remedial action to his own work. The responsibility where work packages overlap can be less clear and the cost of rectification may fall on the client unless specific provision is made in the contract arrangements.

ADVANTAGES AND DISADVANTAGES

Construction management offers the potential advantages of management contracting. In addition it establishes direct relationships between client and trade contractor and thus permits a high degree of involvement and control. On the other hand, it is subject to the same considerations as management contracting regarding risk and the degree of experience required of the client, probably increasing both.

It is used primarily by experienced clients who are able to take part fully in the construction process, on large or complex projects where time is important.

CONTRACT DOCUMENTATION

As yet (July 1995) there is no agreed standard form of contract for construction management or other supporting documentation. Proprietary forms are offered by construction managers which include the agreement for their own appointment.

FIGURE 6.10   DESIGN AND BUILD - ORGANISATIONAL RELATIONSHIPS

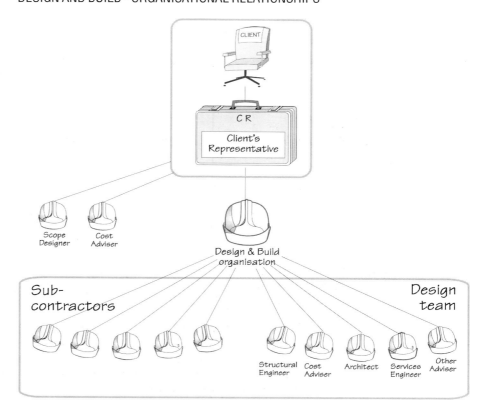

[DESIGN AND BUILD]

SINGLE POINT SERVICE

Increasingly the would-be client is looking for a single organisation to design and provide his building. There is a variety of ways in which this can be achieved:

- *Design and Build*
  - Contractor's total design
  - *Develop and construct*
- System Package
- *Design and Manage.*

These arrangements make it possible to buy a comprehensive service which includes both design and construction, and sometimes other specialist expertise. The approach should be considered where the client:

- requires maximum responsibility to be taken by a single organisation or person
- has a clearly defined brief that is unlikely to change
- has critical time targets
- needs early price clarity.

Single point service can offer both speed and a reasonable degree of choice and design flexibility. The *design and build organisation* providing the service must be carefully chosen and the approach genuinely suitable for the project.

FIGURE 6.11   DESIGN AND BUILD - CONTRACTUAL RELATIONSHIPS

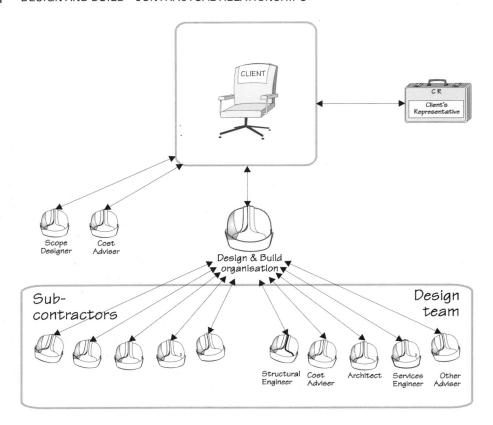

[DESIGN AND BUILD]

DESIGN AND BUILD

KEY FEATURES

Contractual relationships closely reflect the organisational relationships, with the design and build organisation as the single point of responsibility to the client (Figures 6.10 and 6.11).

There are two principal approaches, depending on the extent to which the client wishes to retain control of the design:

* **Contractor's total design**: this limits client involvement to the bare essentials of developing the brief and decision making
* **Develop and construct**: an outline design is provided for the client by a *'scope designer'*, prior to tendering and development of the design by the design and build organisation. This approach makes a greater call on the client's own resources.

CONTRACTOR'S TOTAL DESIGN

The design and build organisation undertakes the entire design and construction process. This may include the feasibility study (usually undertaken for an agreed fee). Other services such as financial advice, land purchase, and funding facilities can also be provided.

FIGURE 6.12   SEQUENCE: CONTRACTOR'S TOTAL DESIGN

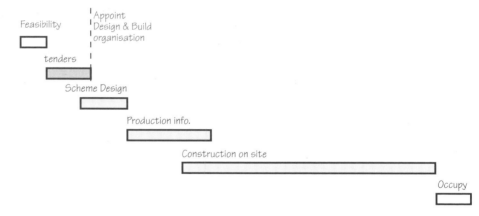

Some companies who specialise in this type of work employ in-house design teams. Others set up specific arrangements for each project, employing external design teams. These are managed as if they were part of the design and build organisation.

DEVELOP AND CONSTRUCT

'Develop and construct' is commonly known as such because the design and build organisation's contribution to the design process is primarily in developing the *construction information* from the client's scheme design.

The client selects and appoints his own advisers, as the scope design team, which takes the project to scheme design stage and gives cost advice. This allows the opportunity to get the basic design right before entering contractual commitment to the design and build organisation. It also provides a good basis for competitive tenders.

[DESIGN AND BUILD]

The selected design and build organisation then completes the design and builds the project. It may agree to take on the scope design team by the process of *novation* and take full responsibility for them and their work beyond the stage already reached. However, where the contractor uses his own designers, the scope design team plays no further part in the design itself. Under JCT form of contract the client must provide an *employer's agent* to oversee the works on his behalf. This might be done by retaining the scope design team in this capacity.

FIGURE 6.13   SEQUENCE: DEVELOP AND CONSTRUCT

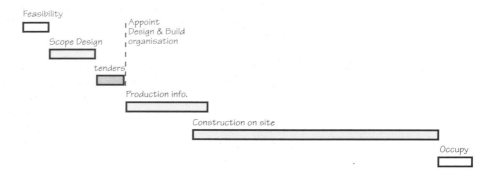

ROLES
THE CLIENT

Design and build arrangements make most demands of the client at the start of the project when the design is being developed and contractual arrangements are being set up. At this stage important decisions usually have to be made quickly, and once made are difficult or expensive to change.

If the potential of design and build is to be realised, the clients' requirements must be very clearly identified and frozen at an early stage. The client must also ensure that the contract documents clearly specify time constraints and quality standards. The intending client must carefully consider his ability to fulfil these requirements before entering a design and build procurement arrangement, and if necessary appoint appropriate advisers.

THE DESIGN AND BUILD
ORGANISATION

Once the contract has been placed, the design and build organisation takes the lead. It is responsible to the client for all aspects of the project for which it has tendered, including:

- progress of design work beyond the point reached at tender stage
- the quality and integrity of the corporate design, as built
- the progress and quality of the construction work

Subject to contractual arrangements for changes and other adjustments, the design and build organisation has to complete the project within the tendered cost to the client.

TENDERING
PROCEDURES

Clients must ensure that good practice is observed in inviting tenders, in particular that industry codes of procedure are followed. It is essential to allow adequate time for tendering. Figures 6.12 and 6.13 indicate the points at which tenders are sought in the overall process.

[DESIGN AND BUILD]

CONTRACTOR'S
TOTAL DESIGN

Tendering on the basis of contractor's total design is complex and expensive for the tenderers. It is therefore recommended practice to use two-stage tendering, particularly where extensive design and investigative work is required.

First stage tenders, based upon outline information only, create an early shortlist of the two or three organisations most suitable to submit more detailed proposals for final selection.

DEVELOP AND CONSTRUCT

Single-stage tenders are more realistic with a develop and construct arrangement, since scheme design stage will have already been reached. Tendering on the same basic design also makes the comparison of tenders more straightforward.

BASIS OF TENDER

The tender is based upon the *employer's requirements*. These include the client's brief which identifies the accommodation needs, performance standards, and any particular requirements as to method. The fuller the proposal at tender stage the less room there is for ambiguity or misunderstanding later on. This is particularly important when tenderers are invited to submit alternative design proposals with apparent cost savings to the client.

Tender conditions normally require contractors to provide details of:

- design proposals
- how they intend to set about the work
- costs (including any charges for the work if it does not proceed to completion)

The selection of the successful tenderer must be based upon a full appraisal of the total package offered, not just upon price. It is worth taking independent expert advice when drafting and evaluating tenders.

ACCEPTANCE

Contractual commitment occurs earlier than with the more traditional forms of procurement. This means it is essential really to understand the proposals and be sure that they fully meet requirements. Late changes are difficult and expensive to implement.

CONTROL SYSTEMS
COSTS

Once engaged, the design and build organisation is responsible for developing the scheme and for its cost. Further independent advice at this stage will help to ensure good value for money.

When the scheme and price have been agreed and written into the contract, the project costs should not alter, unless the contract contains specific provision for *fluctuating prices* or if the client changes his requirements. It may be sensible to include provision for price variation for any major high risk item, for example foundations when ground conditions are known to be unreliable. This allows such risks to be shared and should avoid the design and build organisation from pricing the item at a premium to cover the risk.

TIME

The standard forms of contract specify a completion date and oblige the design and build organisation to provide a detailed programme and

[DESIGN AND BUILD]

progress reports. Although the organisation has a vested interest in keeping to the schedule, particularly if *Liquidated and Ascertained Damages* are required for late delivery, the client should still insist upon regular reports highlighting any change to the contract end date.

QUALITY

The quality requirements for design and build contracts define:

- the project objectives and constraints
- the client's accommodation requirements
- performance standards for the building and equipment.

The design and build organisation is at liberty to offer any suitable design, material or piece of equipment that meets the specification. The client cannot refuse to accept anything that conforms.

In theory, a client is not entitled to use a clerk of works to comment upon any unsatisfactory building work. However, in practice, using a clerk of works can have advantages for both parties and is seldom objected to by the design and build organisation.

PAYMENTS OF FEES AND CONTRACT COSTS

The design and build organisation may be entitled to fees for any initial development work but these are usually payable only if the scheme does not go ahead. The design and build organisation is usually paid in instalments on the completion of agreed stages of work set out in the detailed *activity schedule*. You may wish to use your advisers to confirm that the stages have been properly reached.

ADVANTAGES AND DISADVANTAGES

The design and build approach offers the client:

- a single clear point of responsibility for both design and construction
- the opportunity to transfer more of the design risk
- potential cost and time savings through integration and overlap of design and construction processes
- clarity of final cost early in the project.

Potential disadvantages include:

- fewer firms are available who are skilled to do this type of work
- the contractor's total design arrangement requires a contractual commitment before the scheme design is fully developed.
- the commercial pressures within the design and build organisation can create a compromise in quality standards, particularly in design
- design standards may be difficult to define in the first place which can lead to disappointment or disputes over remedial work
- it is essential that the client is able to achieve a clear and complete picture of his needs prior to tendering; late changes in the brief can be difficult and expensive to accommodate.

SUPPORTING CONTRACT DOCUMENTATION

There are standard forms of contract for design and build arrangements. Associated documentation to appoint advisers and make other contract arrangements is also available. As yet, this does not fully cater without some adaptation for all the variations that may be required.

[DESIGN AND BUILD]

THE SYSTEM PACKAGE

The system package is a design and build approach in which a company offers complete buildings made to its own system. The choice ranges from simple 'sheds' to modular buildings of two or more storeys. However, the flexibility of response to clients needs is not nearly as great as with a purpose-made solution.

The service usually includes obtaining the essential permissions required to build, and the actual erection of the building. Preparatory site work including such essentials as drains, foundations and roads is sometimes excluded and will have to be undertaken separately by a general builder.

The suitability of a system package needs to be examined with great care. Systems that may appear very similar can vary considerably when it comes to durability. It is therefore often worth appointing an adviser to help with selection. If the project is at all complicated the client will need more help with programming and site preparation work.

DESIGN AND MANAGE

The key feature of design and manage is that a single organisation manages the whole of the design and construction process for a fee, with both design and construction on site being undertaken by others. It thus combines some of the features of the fee-based 'management' approaches with some of those of design and build.

There is no standard documentation, nor even a generally accepted definition of design and manage procedures. Depending on the precise contractual arrangements it could be compared most closely with either management contracting or construction management, with the balance of advantages and disadvantages to the client depending the particular allocation of risks and responsibilities.

The design and manage route would normally be taken only by experienced clients, on the basis of careful consideration of specific proposals.

FIGURE 6.14

The choices: a summary

CR
Client's Representative

MULTI POINT
[Divided reponsibility]

The Client enters into separate contracts for various aspects of design and construction, so dividing responsibility for the finished building

DESIGNER-LED

The traditional form of contracting where the Design Team lead the design and construction process

MANAGEMENT CONTRACTING

The Builder is appointed on a fee basis well before work starts on site to assist and advise the design team. He is responsible for the construction work carried out by separate works contractors

CONSTRUCTION MANAGEMENT

A construction expert is is appointed early on, for a fee, to manage the construction process. He supervises the trade contractors, and may coordinate the work of the design team.

SINGLE STAGE

All stages follow sequentially. A single Builder tenders on fully designed information

TWO STAGE

1st stage tenders invited before information complete. 2nd stage tenders usually complete before work starts on site.

SUITABLE FOR:

Most sizes of project from very small to large. Consider Managment if complex	Larger projects where the early involvement of the Builder is needed	Really only suitable for large and complex projects, with experienced clients	Really only suitable for large or complex projects, with experienced clients

SPEED

Probably the slowest of all the arrangements	Can be faster than single stage	Allows for considerable overlapping of activities. Can achieve good speed	Allows for considerable overlapping of activities can achieve good speed.

QUALITY

Opportunity to achieve good quality	Opportunity to achieve good quality	Good quality can be achieved but speed may influence what is possible	Good quality can be achieved but speed may influence what is possible

COST CERTAINTY

Costs are known before contract commitment but design MUST be complete.	Costs are known before the final commitment to the 2nd stage tender	Work starts on site on basis of a cost plan estimate	Work starts on site on basis of a cost plan estimate

FLEXIBILITY

Limited in flexibility, some small variations possible.	Can allow some flexibility to be built in to contract before commitment	This arrangement is offers some flexibility for change in the course of the project	This arrangement offers some flexibility for change in the course of the project

RESPONSIBILITY/ RISK

Responsibilities clear and reasonably shared	Responsibility clear and reasonably shared	The client carries more risk than with the more traditional methods	The client carries high level of responsibility and risk but also receives the benefits

FIGURE 6.14

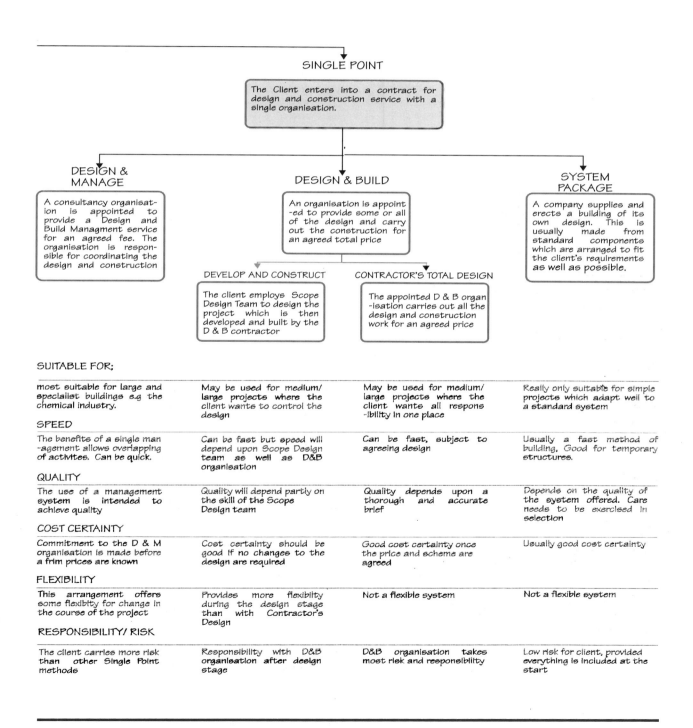

SINGLE POINT

The Client enters into a contract for design and construction service with a single organisation.

DESIGN & MANAGE

A consultancy organisation is appointed to provide a Design and Build Managment service for an agreed fee. The organisation is responsible for coordinating the design and construction

DESIGN & BUILD

An organisation is appoint-ed to provide some or all of the design and carry out the construction for an agreed total price

DEVELOP AND CONSTRUCT

The client employs Scope Design Team to design the project which is then developed and built by the D & B contractor

CONTRACTOR'S TOTAL DESIGN

The appointed D & B organ-isation carries out all the design and construction work for an agreed price

SYSTEM PACKAGE

A company supplies and erects a building of its own design. This is usually made from standard components which are arranged to fit the client's requirements as well as possible.

SUITABLE FOR:			
most suitable for large and specialist buildings e.g the chemical industry.	May be used for medium/ large projects where the client wants to control the design	May be used for medium/ large projects where the client wants all respons -ibility in one place	Really only suitable for simple projects which adapt well to a standard system
SPEED			
The benefits of a single man -agement allows overlapping of activites. Can be quick.	Can be fast but speed will depend upon Scope Design team as well as D&B organisation	Can be fast, subject to agreeing design	Usually a fast method of building. Good for temporary structures.
QUALITY			
The use of a management system is intended to achieve quality	Quality will depend partly on the skill of the Scope Design team	Quality depends upon a thorough and accurate brief	Depends on the quality of the system offered. Care needs to be exercised in selection
COST CERTAINTY			
Commitment to the D & M organisation is made before a frim prices are known	Cost certainty should be good if no changes to the design are required	Good cost certainty once the price and scheme are agreed	Usually good cost certainty
FLEXIBILITY			
This arrangement offers some flexibty for change in the course of the project	Provides more flexibity during the design stage than with Contractor's Design	Not a flexible system	Not a flexible system
RESPONSIBILITY/ RISK			
The client carries more risk than other Single Point methods	Responsibility with D&B organisation after design stage	D&B organisation takes most risk and responsibility	Low risk for client, provided everything is included at the start

APPENDICES

APPENDIX 1
GLOSSARY: DEFINITIONS AND WHO'S WHO

The definitions provided by British Standard 6100 - 'Glossary of building and civil engineering terms' are the formal industry standard descriptions. The definitions that follow are intended to illuminate the usage in this guide. In some cases these differ from BS 6100 "Glossary of building and civil engineering terms".

ACTIVITY SCHEDULE
Detailed analysis of the contract sum in a design and build contract to enable regular progress payments to be made.

ADVISER
Firm or individual who provides advisory, design or other service distinct from carrying out actual construction work. Commonly referred to as a 'consultant' or as providing a 'professional' service.

AGENT
Person appointed with responsibility and authority to act on behalf of another.

ARCHITECT
Designs buildings; particularly trained to provide creative and intellectual input, embracing aesthetic and functional considerations, and an understanding of the importance of user requirements. Most commonly the design team leader, integrating the works of specialist disciplines and the cost adviser. Also normally the contract administrator, superintending construction. Can have particular skills in new-build,and/ or adapting existing buildings, and/ or repair and maintenance.

ARTICLES OF AGREEMENT
Details of contract agreement.

ATTENDANCE
Provision by a builder of facilities and services such as scaffolding and temporary electrical power on a construction site, for use by subcontractors or works contractors.

BILL OF QUANTITIES
Contract document listing items of work measured according to a 'Standard Method of Measurement', used in compiling tender bids and as a basis for pricing variations.

BILL OF APPROXIMATE QUANTITIES
Contract document prepared and used similarly to a bill of quantities but where the quantities are approximate because the design and specifications are not yet complete. All work then needs to be remeasured as designed and constructed.

BRIEF
A full and detailed description of the client's requirements for a building agreed with the design team leader or others responsible for the design.

BUILDABILITY
The extent to which the design of a building takes account of ease of construction.

BUILDER
Construction company undertaking building work, under contract to the client. Named the 'Contractor' in standard forms of contract, and commonly referred to as such.

BUILDER'S CLAIM
A term not appearing the standard forms of contract but commonly used for a request by the builder to be paid sums other than through the measured final account. For example, standard forms provide for the builder to recover proven direct loss and expense as a result of instructions given on behalf of the client.

BUILDING ENVELOPE
The external watertight shell of a building.

BUILDING REGULATIONS
Statutory requirements to which buildings must conform, aimed primarily at safety and public protection.

BUILDING SERVICES ENGINEER
Designer and supervisor of works of public health, electrical and mechanical engineering in an area becoming established as 'environmental engineering'. Many engineers tend to specialise, so several engineers with different specialisms may need to be employed on a highly serviced project.

BUILDING SURVEYOR
Surveyor trained in building construction and law; may be employed as design team leader principally on works of refurbishment and complex alterations of existing buildings. Often undertakes the detailed costing of his own projects and can act as the contract administrator.

CERTIFICATE

Formal document issued by the contract administrator confirming that key stages defined in the contract have been reached.

CHANGE

A change in the employer's requirements in a design and build contract; supplementary provisions in the JCT81 contract require the builder to offer proposals for the client's consideration which include the full cost and programme implications of proposed changes.

CIVIL ENGINEER

Designer and supervisor of civil engineering works, ie roads, reservoirs, waterways etc, having contractual relationship with the client and builder similar to the architect. (c.f. structural engineer.)

CLERK OF WORKS

Client's site inspector, monitoring standards of workmanship and materials, reporting to the contract administrator.

CLIENT

The person or organisation responsible for procuring the construction works, paying for them, and owning the completed building. Referred to as the 'employer' in standard forms of contract.

CLIENT'S REPRESENTATIVE

Person nominated by the client to represent his interests and be the point of communication with the other parties involved in the project. Usually a direct employee with a coordinating role within the client's organisation, with access and accountability to senior management.

COLLATERAL WARRANTY

A parallel agreement with a third party entered into by one of the parties to a subcontract, in order to give the third party a means of legal redress in respect of design or construction carried out under the contract (see also design warranty).

COMMISSIONING

The process by which the various items of the building's machinery and services are witness-tested and set to work to specified standards.

CONSTRUCTION INFORMATION

See production information.

CONSTRUCTION MANAGEMENT

A procurement system in which a construction manager co-ordinates and directs 'trade contractors', each of which has a contract directly with the client to carry out a package of construction work on site (c.f. management contracting).

CONSTRUCTION MANAGER

Term used in construction management projects for the construction expert employed on fee basis to direct and co-ordinate work on site, but without a direct contractual relationship with the trade contractors.

CONSTRUCTION TEAM

The builder's site organisation headed by a site agent or project manager comprising programmers, planners, quality controllers, surveyors, general and trades supervisors.

CONTRACT ADMINISTRATOR

The person, usually but not necessarily an architect, surveyor or engineer, named in contract with the builder for the purpose of giving instructions to the builder and administering the contract on the client's behalf. Also known as the supervising officer under certain standard forms of contract.

CONTRACTOR'S PROPOSALS

The basis of a tender offer by a design and build organisation in response to the employer's requirements. Once accepted they are incorporated into the contract documents.

COST ADVISER

Responsible for giving advice on cost aspects of design and specification proposals, methods of procurement etc., normally a quantity surveyor. May provide advice either as a part of the design team or directly to the client.

COST PLAN

An analysis, element by element, of the proposed building agreed by the design team as a distribution of the client's budget and against which the cost of the developing design is monitored.

COST REIMBURSEMENT CONTRACT

A contract whereby by the builder recovers all the costs of labour, materials and plant necessarily incurred in carrying out the work. Commonly referred to as 'cost plus' contract as the builder is paid a fixed or variable fee to cover his profit and overheads.

DEFECTS LIABILITY PERIOD

A pre-agreed period, commonly 12 months starting from practical completion, during which the builder is required to remedy, at his own expense, all genuine defects appearing in the building. The contract administrator issues a certificate of making good defects when the final list is cleared.

DESIGN AND BUILD

Procurement system in which a single organisation takes responsibility not only for construction work but also for s design as built.

DESIGN AND BUILD ORGANISATION

Organisation contracted to carry out a design and build project; usually but not necessarily a builder.

DESIGN AND MANAGE CONTRACT

Procurement system that combines the characteristics of design and build and either construction management or management contracting.

DESIGN TEAM

Term, usually used in the context of procurement systems with multipoint responsibility to the client, to describe the group of advisers responsible for the design of the building. Normally but not necessarily taken to include the cost adviser.

DESIGN TEAM LEADER

Designer responsible for coordinating the work of the design team; usually an architect, but may be a building surveyor or engineer.

DESIGN WARRANTY

Agreement entered into by specialist designers with the client collateral to the building contract. Introduced partly to circumvent the limitations of consequential loss recovery under the law of negligence.

DESIGNER-LED PROCUREMENT

Procurement arrangement in which design is carried out by a professional designer or team engaged by the client, prior to the client entering a contract with a builder to carry out the construction work as designed. Commonly referred to as 'traditional' procurement.

DEVELOP AND CONSTRUCT

Variant of design and build where the employer's requirements issued to the tenderers include a firm scheme design, subsequently developed in the contractor's proposals.

DOMESTIC SUBCONTRACTOR

Subcontractor provided and employed by the builder. Under the standard forms of contract the contract administrator has the opportunity to approve all such subcontractors.

EMPLOYER

Term used for client in standard forms of contract.

EMPLOYER'S AGENT

Person named to act on behalf of the client in a design and build contract. Has implied authority given by the general law of agency to commit the client, but this authority is limited by the terms of the standard forms of contract.

ENGINEER

See 'building services engineer', 'civil engineer', 'structural engineer'.

EMPLOYER'S REQUIREMENTS

A detailed brief issued to design & build tenderers including performance specifications for all aspects of the work and varying degrees of outline design. Once clarified to match the accepted 'contractor's proposals' they become a contract document.

ENVIRONMENTAL ENGINEER

See building services engineer

EXTENDED COMPLETION DATE

Revised contract completion date which takes account of extensions of time awarded under the contract.

EXTENSION OF TIME

Addition to the contract period granted by the contract administrator on application by the builder that the works are being delayed by one of the specified events set out in the contract as beyond his control.

FACILITIES MANAGER

Person responsible for taking over and running the completed building, with particular reference to environmental services. His task may include other aspects of the building management and maintenance.

'FAST-TRACK'

Term given to a project which employs techniques that are positively aimed at accelerating the progress of the work to meet very tight time- scales by overlapping design and construction.

FEASIBILITY STUDY

Early stage exercise to evaluate options in the client's brief in terms of time, money and what is physically achievable, with recommendations for proceeding.

FINAL ACCOUNT

The agreed adjusted contract sum allowing for the cost of all variations and other instructions including remeasurement of work covered by approximate quantities and provisional sums.

FINAL CERTIFICATE

Certificate issued by the contract administrator to the effect that the builder has carried out all his contractual obligations.

FIXED PRICE CONTRACT

A contract where the builder's prices are fixed for the duration of the works. The tender includes amounts the builder considers will cover inflation in the prices of labour, materials and plant.

FLUCTUATING PRICE CONTRACT

A contract where the builder's prices are adjusted for inflation, usually by the application of a formula and published indices.

FORM OF CONTRACT

Printed standard forms of building contract, including many devised by the Joint Contracts Tribunal (JCT), a body representing most of the professional and trade organisations concerned with building.

HANDOVER

Procedure by which the client takes over the building following issue of the practical completion certificate. The method should be specified in the contract documents.

INSPECTOR

Term used for clerk of works for building engineering services (see also resident engineer).

INSTRUCTIONS

Written directions given to a builder by a contract administrator or employer's agent which have contractual consequences.

INTERIM CERTIFICATE

Certificate issued by the contract administrator or employer's agent stating the amount of payment due under the building contract and which must be honoured by the client. Usually issued monthly or on completion of pre-agreed work stages.

LANDSCAPE ARCHITECT

A specialist in landscape design and horticulture but not in building as such.

LATENT DEFECTS

Building defects which appear after practical completion and which are subject to the Limitation Acts.

LIQUIDATED AND ASCERTAINED DAMAGES

Genuine pre-estimate of the losses that the client believes he will suffer from any delay to completion, usually expressed in amounts per week. Only levied when delay is for reasons which do not entitle the builder to an extension of time.

LUMP SUM CONTRACT

Contract placed on the basis of an all-inclusive contract sum, usually implying a tender based on a fully worked-out design (c.f. cost reimbursement contract).

MANAGEMENT CONTRACTING

Procurement system in which the builder is paid on a fee basis to manage the construction process, with all construction work on site carried out under subcontract to the builder by 'works contractors'.

MANAGEMENT CONTRACTOR

The builder in management contracting procurement.

MEASUREMENT CONTRACT

Contract where the agreed contract sum is based upon a bill of approximate quantities and recalculated following remeasurement of the work as designed, and instructed on site.

MULTIPOINT PROCUREMENT

Arrangement where the client enters into contracts with a number of different organisations for design and construction, so dividing responsibilities for the finished building.

NEGOTIATED TENDER

Procedure for appointing builder and agreeing a contract sum on the basis of negotiation rather than a tendered amount. The negotiation may be based on a previous competitive price, for example for a similar and successfully completed contract which the builder had won in competition.

NOMINATED SUBCONTRACTOR

Specialist contractor nominated by the contract administrator following selection, usually through competitive tendering, and with whom the builder, as 'main contractor', is required to enter into formal subcontract agreements. The standard forms of contract enable the client to make separate agreements with nominated subcontractors with particular reference to design warranties.

NOVATION

Transfer of contractual rights and obligations from one party to another, including the transfer of a scope design team and their work from client to a design & build organisation.

PACKAGE DEAL

All-in contractual arrangement for building procurement used particularly where the client's needs can be met by a standard predesigned product.

PLAN OF WORK

A standard, systematic, stage by stage analysis of the work involved in designing and supervising building work. Facilitates the clear-cut appointment and payment of advisers.

PRACTICAL COMPLETION CERTIFICATE

Certificate issued by the contract administrator stating that, in his opinion, the work is for all practical purposes complete. While not being necessarily complete in every respect, the building should be safe and capable of occupation. The issue of this certificate represents a significant contractual milestone.

PRIME COST

Cost of building without addition of profit. A 'prime cost contract' involves the reimbursement of a builder's costs of labour, materials and plant with an agreed percentage to cover profit and overheads.

PROCUREMENT

The process of obtaining building work, from deciding to proceed with construction to accepting the completed work.

PRODUCTION INFORMATION

Stage in the plan of work which involves the production of working drawings, specifications and, where appropriate, bill of quantities, all intended to enable the builder to carry out construction. Also known as 'construction information'.

PROFESSIONAL INDEMNITY

Insurance policy taken out by design team members which indemnifies them against action by the client to recover costs resulting from defective design.

PROJECT MANAGER

Building professional able to take responsibility for coordinating and managing all aspects of the building procurement process, from inception to completion. Individuals may come from a range of backgrounds.

PROVISIONAL SUMS

Sums included by the design team in the tender documents to allow for work not yet designed or specified.

RETENTION

Sum built up of amounts retained from interim payments (not normally exceeding 5% of the contract sum) intended to secure due performance of the works. On Practical Completion half the fund is released and the remainder held pending making good of defects in the ensuing defects liability period.

QUALITY MANAGEMENT SYSTEM

Framework of procedures and working practices aimed at ensuring that an organisation provides works and services of an appropriate consistent quality. A firm's quality management system may be registered as complying with the requirements of BS EN ISO 9000 (BS 5750), covering all or a defined part of the firm's activities.

QUANTITY SURVEYOR

Traditionally the person who 'measures', that is quantifies, building works and has developed skills of estimating prices, negotiation and cost analysis of buildings. Will usually advise design team and client on contractual and financial arrangements for the project. Administers financial aspects of the building contract.

RESIDENT ENGINEER

Individual carrying out function of clerk of works in relation to services or structural engineering aspects of a building contract. Normally employed by services or structural engineer.

RISK MANAGEMENT

Systematic approach to the identification, assessment and management of risk. Established as a discipline in its own right, but if required it should be available within the portfolio of skills of your building advisers.

SCHEDULE OF RATES

Fully itemised list of building works priced by tenderers and used as a basis for pricing remeasurement works or for valuing variations where no bill of quantities have been supplied. The schedule should be attached to the specifications as a contract document.

SCHEME DESIGN

Stage in the plan of work when the general arrangement, construction and specification for the building is produced with the cost plan for the client's further consideration. A vital stage irrespective of the procurement route followed.

SCOPE DESIGN TEAM

Design team employed by the client to prepare a scheme design when procurement is by a develop and construct arrangement.

SELECTIVE TENDERING

Inviting competitive tenders from a short list of contractors selected for their suitability, considering the size and type of the project.

SERVICES ENGINEER

See 'building services engineer'

SINGLE POINT PROCUREMENT

Arrangement whereby the client enters into a single contract for the design and construction of the building with an organisation that accepts responsibility for the full design, including where operating on a develop and construct basis.

SITE DEVELOPMENT WORKS

Roads, sewers,services and other infrastructure works sometimes let as a separate contract. Also known as site preparation.

SPECIFICATION

The technical description used to set the standards and type of construction.

STRUCTURAL ENGINEER

An engineer who specialises in the design of building structures. May undertake role of design team leader for projects with a high structural engineering content. Otherwise a commonly used skill within the design team.

SUPERVISING OFFICER

See 'contract administrator'

TARGET COST

Amount agreed with a management contractor or construction manager as the likely final cost of a project where design work is incomplete and works contracts are still to be let. Acts as an incentive to economy where the management fee is fixed.

TRADITIONAL PROCUREMENT

Procurement arrangement in which advisers are appointed by the client to design the building, and to prepare tender documents for a building contract let on the basis of this design. Referred to in this guide as 'designer-led, multipoint procedure'.

TECHNOLOGY SPECIALIST

Expert engaged on the recommendation of the design team leader to advise on special requirements, for example, on the performance of the building envelope.

TRADE CONTRACTOR

Contractor employed to carry out construction works under the construction management method of procurement, under direct contract to the client.

TWO - STAGE TENDER

Procedure allowing early engagement of the builder. The first stage involves selection through competition on limited information. The second stage is negotiation with the selected builder as design work is completed, using a pricing structure submitted with the first stage tender.

VALUE MANAGEMENT

A structured approach to the management of projects, from inception through to handover and use of the building, with the objective of achieving best value for money. In particular it is characterised by a facilitated, problem-solving methodology and the use of multi-disciplinary workshops.

VARIATION

Instruction issued by the contract administrator to the builder for additions or alterations to the works described in the contract.

WORKS CONTRACTOR

Contractor employed to carry out construction works under the management contracting method of procurement, under subcontract to the management contractor.

APPENDIX 2
USEFUL NAMES AND ADDRESSES

Association of Consultant Architects   (ACA)
Buchanans Wharf, Redcliff Backs, Bristol, BS1 6HT
Tel 01272 293379

Association of Consulting Engineers   (ACE)
Alliance House,
12 Caxton Street, London SW1H 0QL Tel 0171 222 6557
Practice advice, appointments, fees

Association of Project Managers   (APM)
85 Oxford Road, High Wycombe, Bucks HP11 2DX
Tel 01494 440090

British Property Federation   (BPF)
35 Catherine Place, London SW1E 6DY Tel 0171 828 0111
Association of the largest property developers and building
owners

British Standards Institution   (BSI)
2 Park Street, London W1A 2BS Tel 0171 629 9000
3 York Street, Manchester M2 2AT Tel 0161 832 3731
Publishes product standards, design standards, methods
of test and assessment

Building Centre
26 Store Street, London WC1E 7BT Tel 0171 637 1022

Building Employers Confederation   (BEC)
82 New Cavendish Street, London W1M 8AD Tel 0171 580
5588
Principal organisation of major contractors representing the
building industry in England and Wales

Building Services Research and
Information Association   (BSRIA)
Old Bracknell Lane West, Bracknell, Berks RG12 7AH
Tel 01344 426511

Building Structures Group (BSG)
4 Whitehall Court, Westminster, London SW1A 2ES
Tel 0171 839 8566
Umbrella organisation for specialist contractors for building frame and envelope

Central Unit on Procurement   (CUP)
HM Treasury Allington Towers, 19 Allington Street,
London SW1E 5EB Tel 0171 270 1638

Chartered Institute of Arbitrators   (CIArb)
24 Angel Street, City Road, London EC1V 2RS Tel 0171
837 4483

Chartered Institute of Building   (CIOB)
Englemere, Kings Ride, Ascot, Berks SL5 8BJ Tel 01344
23355
Qualifying body and learned society for construction pro-
fessionals, including contractors and project managers

Chartered Institution of Building Services Engineers
(CIBSE)
Delta House, 222 Balham High Road, London SW12 9BS
Tel 0181 675 5211
The principle professional body concerned with mechani-
cal and electrical engineering services. Produces standards,
guides, consultants directory. Disciplinary body

Confederation of British Industry (CBI)
Centre Point, 103 New Oxford Street, London WC1A 1DU
Tel 0171 379 7400

Department of the Environment   (DoE)
Property Advisory Services, St Christopher House, South-
wark Street, London SE1 0TE
Tel 0171 921 2238

Electrical Contractors' Association   (ECA)
ESCA House, 34 Palace Court, Bayswater, London W2 4HY
Tel 0171 229 1266
Trade association of the largest electrical specialist con-
tractors and subcontractors

Electrical Contractors' Association of Scotland
(ECAS)
Bush House, Bush Estate, Mid Lothian, EH26 0SB
Tel 0131 445 5577
Trade association for the major electrical contractors in
Scotland

Federation of Master Builders   (FMB)
Gordon Fisher House, 14-15 Great James Street, London
WC1N 3DP Tel 0171 242 7583
Principal trade association for small and medium size firms
in the building industry

Heating and Ventilating Contractors Association (HVCA)
ESCA House 34 Palace Court, Bayswater, London W2 4JG Tel 0171 229 2488
Trade association for mechancial services contractors

Institute of Clerks of Works   (ICW)
41 The Mall, Ealing, London W5 3TJ Tel 0181 579 2917/8

Institution of Civil Engineers   (ICE)
Great George Street, London SW1P 3AA Tel 0171 222 7722
Learned society, practice advice

Institution of Electrical Engineers   (IEE)
Savoy Place, London WC2R 0BC Tel 0171 240 1871
Practice advice, standards, regulations

Institution of Mechanical Engineers   (IMechE)
1 Birdcage Walk, London SW1H 9JJ Tel 0171 222 7899
Practice advice, standards, regulations

Institution of Structural Engineers   (IStructE)
11 Upper Belgrave Street, London SW1X 8BH Tel 0171 235 4535
Learned society, practice advice

Joint Contracts Tribunal   (JCT)
The Joint Secretaries, 66 Portland Place, London W1N 4AD and 82 New Cavendish Street, London W1M 8AD
Representative of a wide ranging group of those with an interest in building contracts. Produces standard forms of contract and warranty agreements with regular revisions and practice notes.

Landscape Institute
6-7 Barnard Mews, London SW1 1QU Tel 0171 738 9166
The professional Institute for landscape architects, landscape managers, landscape scientists.

National Federation of Demolition Contractors (NFDC)
Resurgam House, 1A New Road, The Causeway, Staines, Middx Tel 01784 456799
Principle trade federation for demolition contractors

National House Building Council (NHBC)
Buildmark House, Chiltern Avenue, Amersham, Bucks HP6 5AP Tel 01494 434477

National Joint Consultative Committee (NJCC)
Secretary 0171 580 5588 Publications available via BEC, RIBA, RIAS RICS
Area organised committee of architects, builders and surveyors principally involved in preparing and issuing practice guides

National Specialist Contractors Council (NSCC)
18 Mansfield Street, London, W1M 9FG
Tel 0171 580 5404
Umbrella organisation for specialist contractors

Royal Incorporation of Architects in Scotland (RIAS)
15 Rutland Square, Edinburgh EH1 2BE Tel 0131 229 7545
The Scottish lead body on all matters pertaining to architecture, client advice and consultancy services

Royal Institute of British Architects   (RIBA)
66 Portland Place, London W1N 4AD Tel 0171 580 5533
The principal professional and learned body representing architects in the UK - practice advice, appointments

Royal Institution of Chartered Surveyors   (RICS)
12 Great George Street, London SW1P 3AD Tel 0171 222 7000
Represents surveyors working in commercial property, construction, infrastructure, minerals, residential and rural property

Scottish Building Contracts Committee (SPCC)
27 Melville Street, Edinburgh, EH3 7GH
Tel 0131 226 2552
Modifies JCT and issues own contract documents

Scottish Building Employers Federation (SBEF)
13 Woodside Cresent, Glasgow, G3 7UP
Tel 0141 332 7144

Scottish Joint Consultative Council   (SJCC)
16 Pendicle Road, Bearsden, Glasgow, G61 1BY
Tel 0141 942 268
Good practice forum for Scotland: endorses or modifies advice of NJCC to accord with Scotish law and practice

APPENDIX 3
A BRIEF MAKING CHECK-LIST

WHAT IT IS FOR

This check-list illustrates the information that you will need to produce if the project goes ahead. It is not exhaustive and is inevitably general. However it should help with testing the initial viability of your proposals and choosing advisers. The more you know about your needs before selecting advisers, the better able you will be to find really suitable people. Once appointed they should provide guidance on what other information is required.

Before examining the details of your project's needs try to define the main reasons why you are intending to build. What are your aspirations? What is it for? Who is going to use it?

The brief has four main elements:

- project requirements
- budget
- programme
- procedures

PROJECT REQUIREMENTS

LOCATION

Are you looking for a new site? If so, what determines the location?
> Does it need to be near specific services or users?
> Does it need to be served by public transport?
> Can it be spread out? Or does it need to be compact?
> What servicing needs will it have? Any special requirements? Material deliveries?
> Is car parking necessary? How much?
> Will it create noise or other potential pollution?
> Is there any contamination of the land?

Your advisers will need to test any site that seems to be appropriate. Their study should take account of the topography, local planning requirements and existing services

SITE

Is it a greenfield site or do you intend to develop an existing site or building?
> What are the terms of ownership?
> Do you know of any restrictions on its uses, such as planning requirements?
> Do you know of any legal or other constraints? Boundaries?
> Is it available?

Your advisers will arrange surveys and any other investigative work but any information on existing conditions should be given to them.

ACCOMMODATION REQUIREMENTS

Are you looking for a flexible building solution?
> Is it to be temporary or permanent?
> Does the building need to be adaptable?
> Are you likely to need to expand in the future?

What are the purposes of all the activities?
> What processes or activities need to be accommodated?
> Who is going to occupy the building?
> Are there critical proximities or sequences?
> Are any of the functions controlled by regulation?

What are the physical requirements of each function?
> How many people?
> Do they require specially controlled environments?
> Special facilities for safety or hygiene?
> Communications systems? Telephone/ computer?
> What services does each need? Power points, water etc?
> What sort of access? Lifts, hoists? Disability?
> Is security important? Where?

What support facilities are likely to be needed ?
> For occupants? Or visitors?
> Toilets? Canteen? Storage?
> Do you have any minimum standards for level of provision?

What performance standards must be met?
> Are there critical dimensions? Height or weight?
> What general levels of heating, lighting, ventilation?
> How much control of these?
> What level of wear and tear? Vandal resistance?
> Ease of maintenance?

What quality of building is required?
> How important is appearance? Style?
> Do you want very good materials? Everywhere?

It is unlikely that you will be able to answer all of these questions in detail. For instance, although you may may know the number of users you may have little idea how much space they will occupy. Don't worry, that's why you employ advisers to help. If, however, you know of something that works well, involve the people who have information about it.
Try to produce information in a methodical and consistent manner. In this way you can also see what you don't know - and need to.

BUDGET

Although you may have only a general idea of the likely cost of the project you will need to consider a funding strategy with your building advisers so that they are aware of the financial limitations.

FUNDING

Does the proposed method of funding have implications for the project?
> Are there costs or interest charges?
> When is funding available?
> Is the funding time-limited?

Is there a maximum funding limit?
> Is it fixed? Or is it related to value of the development?
> Would phasing the work help you to make better use of your resources?

Are you relying on income from your project to help with the funding?
> Does this depend upon rental on completion? Or release of other property elsewhere?
> Will this affect the timing of the work?

COSTS

Have all the likely setting up costs been taken into account?
> Moving? Temporary accommodation?
> New furniture and fittings and equipment?
> Fees? Investigative work? Licences?

What about running costs?
> Taxes, maintenance, insurance, fuel, cleaning?

Advice on the likely financial implications of a project should be taken as early as possible. To assess these you need expenditure cashflow forecasts based on estimated costs.

PROGRAMME

Are there critical factors that determine or influence the programme?
> Related to funding?
> Related to other projects you have in hand?
> Some particular event?

What is your preferred programme for the work?
> Is there an optimum sequence?

When defining the programme tell your advisers why something is important, and let them know if circumstances change. Tight programmes can be achieved but there is often a premium to pay in terms of cost, sacrifice of standards, or increased risk to you.

PROCEDURES

Arrangements for a project vary according to how it is run, the number of people involved and the nature of the client organisation. It is important that on even the smallest job there are agreed ways of doing things and that everyone understands what is expected. You must be satisfied that these arrangements are firmly in place and then stick to them like everyone else.

COMMUNICATIONS

What regular communication arrangements do you want with your advisers?
> Reports? - Progress, financial?
> Meetings?
> What information/ correspondence do you want to receive?

Who is authorised to give instructions on your behalf ?
> Name?
> Limit of authority? For what?
> Procedure for obtaining authority beyond the limit?
> Time scales?
> Authority to proceed to the next stage?

Who is authorised to receive instructions?
> Name?

How is access to be arranged?
> For information? Consultation?
> To existing premises?

MONEY

What arrangements are required for making payments?
> What information required?
> Who is responsible?
> Time limits?

INTERNAL PROCEDURES

Do you have your own internal procedures that must be adhered to?
> Are they available? And up to date?
> Security? Safety?
> Technical standards?

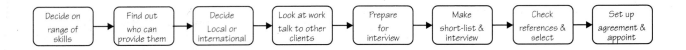

APPENDIX 4
INTERVIEW PROCESS FOR SELECTING ADVISERS

BEFORE YOU START

CONSIDER YOUR OBJECTIVES

You are looking for a person or organisation who will
- positively help to meet your aims
- provide what you want
- manage the process within time and budget
- be dependable and get on well with you

CONSIDER YOUR PRIORITIES

Before seeing what the market offers, outline your key priorities: this will help you focus on what you are looking for. Try answering the questions in Section 5.

CONSIDER WHAT TO LOOK FOR

Use these priorities to establish the principal features that you seek. For instance, if you have identified the need to withstand heavy wear and tear you will be looking for examples of robust design and buildings which have performed well in use.

Remember that the people you will be looking at may all be basically competent but will have different interests, skills and experience.

Previous experience can be a good reason for choosing a particular firm. At least part of the valuable learning process has been done at someone else's expense. On the other hand you may be looking for a fresh approach and want an organisation with a track record of good analysis combined with innovation.

Examples of work are among the best selection criteria. Photographs and illustrations are useful as a starting point. Before the final choice is made try to visit some of their buildings. Talk to the people who were involved in the process, including those who now have to manage and use the building.

LESSONS FROM OTHER BUILDING OWNERS

The following provides a basis for asking about other people's experience of building, to give you pointers to issues to be explored.

What was the method of building procurement?
  Who took part?

Who took the lead ?
Who did they deal with?
What did the client think of the overall service provided?
  Was it efficient?
  Were the communications good?
  Were their requirements responded to?
  Were all the services provided?

What were the client's internal arrangements for making and communicating decisions?
  Did they work?
  How did they arrive at the brief? -Did they get much help?

Who was the project leader ?
  Was the client kept informed of the programme?
  Was it adhered to? - Before and during the building work?
  Were they kept informed of the costs?
  Was the budget adhered to?
  Were there any special difficulties that had to be coped with?

What did the client think of the management of the building work?
  Did it seem efficient?
  Were there any problems?
  Were they resolved quickly?

Is the client pleased with the finished building?
  What it looks like?
  How it works?
  The quality of the workmanship?
  Have there been any problems with the building?

If they had to go through the process again, what changes would they make? Why?

THE SELECTION INTERVIEW

PREPARATION

Draw up a short-list of preferred organisations to lead the project. It is sensible to interview at least three firms but you may wish to see as many as six. If you have not already done so try to obtain information or brochures about their work

Before arranging interviews write a summary outline of your proposals for the project. Your short-listed advisers may want the opportunity to visit the site or building before interview.

Although it is possible to interview them at their offices it is probably more convenient to arrange for them to come to you. You will need to arrange a convenient venue. However, it is advisable to visit the offices of the preferred candidate and meet the people likely to be involved before making a final choice.

Allow enough time for a thorough discussion; this will probably include a short presentation so the process will take between an hour and an hour and a half, and possibly longer. The invitation to interview should include your brief outline proposals and also make clear that you are seeing a number of firms.

STYLE AND CONTENT

The conduct the interview is a matter for personal preference. You may include a formal agenda in your invitation or you may simply ask each firm to present their approach to your project. In any event you will need to cover the full range of relevant topics. (A basic interview check-list follows in this appendix)

It is always helpful to interview with at least one other person. This not only shares the burden of questioning and recording the answers but also brings in different points of view. Anyone in your organisation who is likely to play a key role in running the project should be involved in the selection process.

Each firm you interview will have different strengths and weaknesses. It is vital to concentrate as hard on the important and sometimes difficult topics as on the more obviously attractive aspects of the proposals. Building is expensive and it is your money that will be paying for it. Don't be afraid to ask why a project over-ran or cost more. Consider the answers carefully. Do they ring true? Could you work well with these people? If in any doubt try and find out the answers another way and do not commit yourself until you are satisfied.

MAKING THE SELECTION AND APPOINTMENT

Making your mind up can be difficult. Some find it helpful to use a point scoring system against a fixed set of criteria. In any event, it is wise to use a check list for each interview and ensure that it is properly covered each time. Detailed advice is given in "Value by competition", published by CIRIA.

If you have not already done so, take up references before agreeing to appoint. Ask for a long-list of previous clients and the names of people to contact. From this choose whom to approach. Try to take up references personally.

Face to face, or at least telephone discussions are usually the most frank and enable you to obtain answers to questions that you are unlikely to get in writing.

Once satisfied that you have made the right choice, you need to agree the conditions of appointment. Points that you need to get clear include:

Function and role
  The role the organisation will play depends on the procurement method that you decide to adopt. However it is important to make clear what your expectations are at this stage even if they change by agreement later. If you are making a lead appointment you need to say so now.

Services to be included.
  Go through all the services that the selected firm is to provide.

  Find out what is not included but which may become necessary. Discuss how these could be undertaken.

Basis for charging
  Ask for the basic framework for charges. This should include the normal fees, hourly rates, and other expenses or costs. It may not be possible to agree a precise fee at this stage, as this may depend on how the project develops. If you do not agree a definite fee basis, make sure that you have a firm arrangement for any preliminary work. It is wise to set a fixed budget which can only be exceeded with your specific agreement. Agree methods of payment.

Works stages to be undertaken
  First-time clients are strongly recommended to limit the appointment to the initial work stage with an option to extend as the work proceeds. Although you may find this proposal is resisted it is a perfectly reasonable arrangement and limits your liability in the event of the project not proceeding for some reason - or your finding that you have chosen the wrong firm.

Procedures and administration
  You need to agree ground rules for the management of the project. These should include communications, methods of authorisation for expenditure, any internal procedures or standing orders, instructions and records.

Warranties
  Obtain details of any warranties or professional indemnity insurance. Make sure that these are up to date and adequate.

FEES

The level of fees charged by the design team and other advisers varies enormously - from about 5% to 20% of the actual construction costs (and exceptional fees can be even higher). Between 50% and 55% of the total project fees are normally incurred before a contract is placed with a builder.

A range of different factors affect the fees charged:

* the type of building - can affect total fees by up to 20%
* new work or work to existing buildings - rehabilitation can be up to 50% higher than new construction
* degree of complexity - complex building usually require a greater range of specialists and more coordination
* size - small projects tend to be labour intensive and more expensive in percentage terms
* location - projects in London can be 10% higher than those in the provinces
* individual or team appointment of advisers - team appointments can be 10% less
* duration of project - there is an 'optimum' time for most projects; deviating from this can affect costs
* repetition - can reduce fees.

The these factors should be discussed when fees are negotiated. Your advisers should provide examples of fees for similar work.

If you wish your advisers to agree a fixed ('lump sum') fee, you must be very clear and comprehensive in stating the services you require. Otherwise you are likely to be asked to pay for 'additional services' on a time charge basis.

Setting fee levels by competition can result in lower fees but is likely to be difficult to manage satisfactorily

INTERVIEW CHECK-LIST   NOTES

OFFICE ARRANGEMENTS

		Notes
Location	Are there other branches? What do they do?	
Staffing	Obtain an outline of how the office is managed and a breakdown of directly employed personnel	
What Skills ?	Architects, structural engineers, environmental engineers, surveyors, quantity surveyors, landscape architects, space planners	
Responsibility?	How is the work managed within the office? Who is in charge of a project? Can you ask for particular people to work on a project?	
Technology	Does the firm use computer aided design (CAD) or other new technology in its work? Does it undertake or support research?	
Insurance/warranty	What professional indemnity does the firm carry? What level?	

WORKING ARRANGEMENTS

		Notes
Associations	Does the firm have associations with other firms? What skills? Who is used when there are no in-house skills?	
Preferred methods	Does the firm favour any particular procurement systems? Designer led? Design and build? Construction management?	
Project management	Views on how the project should be managed. Who will take the lead and under what arrangements?	
Control systems	Does the firm operate a QA scheme, if so are they third party certified? How is job programming managed? Approach to cost control? How do they apply the CDM Regulations?	

EXPERIENCE & SERVICES

		Notes
Special skills	Does the firm claim to specialise? If so, in what? Conservation? Building types? Energy management? Are they relevant to your project?	
Experience	What relevant buildings? Other clients? References? Identify one or two examples and discuss how they were managed. What were the key issues? What went well? What did not? Were they finished on time and within budget? If not why not?	
Work Capacity	What is current workload? What resources? Time?	

APPROACH TO YOUR PROJECT

		Notes
Outline proposal	Ideas on how the project should be approached. Who would be involved and under what arrangements? Suggested fee basis? What method of procurement? What sort of programme time?	

APPENDIX 5
TENDER AND SITE START CHECK-LIST

THE PRINCIPLES

Tendering arrangements for the building contract vary widely according to the procurement route followed. What is described below applies particularly to the more traditional designer led arrangements. However, many of the principles involved can be applied to other methods.

PRE-TENDER ARRANGEMENTS

SETTING UP THE CONTRACT DETAILS

Your advisers will need to include the contract conditions and working arrangements in the tender invitation. Of particular interest to you are:

THE CONTRACT CONDITIONS

The form of contract proposed
The contract period and any phasing
The length of the defects liability period
The level of liquidated and ascertained damages
Any warranty arrangements
Any proposed alterations to the standard form which increase the risk to you
Insurances

WORKING ARRANGEMENTS

Possession and site access arrangements
Location of storage and plant
Protection of existing features and reinstatement
Hours of working
Commisioning of equipment
Special requirements
Health andSafety Plan

It is important that you see and agree all this information before tenders are sought. You must insist on this even if time is very short.

CONFIRMING READINESS FOR TENDERING

Inviting tenders with incomplete information is a potential risk that must be avoided. It is good practice to ask your principal adviser or the design team leader to certify that the information is ready and sufficiently complete for the purpose of inviting tenders. The process should include an update on the statutory consents required before building starts and assurance that none of these will cause delay later. This is not always possible if the programme is particularly tight. You need to discuss with your advisers the possible consequences if things do not go according to plan.

SELECTION OF SHORT LIST TO TENDER

You may be happy to leave the short-listing of tenderers to your advisers, or wish to form your own opinion of their suitability for the work. In any case, expect to receive a formal report with evidence of suitability in support of the selection. You will be required to approve the recommended shortlist and agree the details of how the tendering process is to be carried out.

ON RECEIPT OF TENDERS

TENDER REPORTS

You should receive an analysis of the tenders received and recommendations regarding acceptance. It is not uncommon for the design team to meet the preferred tenderer before a final report is made to you.

SIGNING OFF THE DESIGN

You should ensure that you understand the design and its implications prior to entering into any contracts for construction. This is the last opportunity to raise significant queries; major changes made later are likely to be costly. If receipt of tenders or other events make apparent a need for savings or other changes, make sure you are happy with the revised scheme.

CONTRACT MANAGEMENT ARRANGEMENTS

Go through the arrangements for running the contract and any duties that you as client will be required to perform. One of these will be making payments as the work proceeds. Make sure that the cashflow is up-to- date and that your own arrangements for obtaining funding are in place.

If a clerk of works or other inspector is required, make sure that the necessary appointments have been made and methods of payment agreeed.

INSURANCE

You may need special insurances to cover your part of the works or contents. Check what is required and that you are fully covered.

ENTERING INTO A CONTRACT

Do not give your approval to enter into any contract until you are fully satisfied that everything is ready and that you are able to meet your financial obligations.

APPENDIX 6
COMPLETION & HANDOVER CHECK-LIST

HANDOVER
PRACTICAL COMPLETION

Practical completion has immediate consequences. The builder:

- is protected from the imposition of liquidated and ascertained damages beyond the date of practical completion
- no longer has a right of access to your building
- becomes responsible for making good defects and the defects liability period starts to run

And you become responsible for:

- certain insurances which are transferred to you
- the security and maintenance of the building

PLANNING FOR COMPLETION

WHEN TO START

You have to start planning for the completion and handover of your project as soon as you decide to proceed with it. During the briefing and design stages you will be making decisions about materials and equipment. By making these decisions you are also accepting the responsibility for maintenance, servicing, and day to day management. In some cases this may be minimal, in others there may be considerable financial and human resource implications.

As soon as briefing begins you need to sort out with your advisers the principles of how handover is to be achieved: information you need to receive and arrangements for familiarisation with the equipment and systems installed. There may be some additional cost in providing what you want.

PREPARING FOR OCCUPATION

The practicalities of occupation need to be considered from the start. How long will it take to move in? Will additional fitting out be needed after the main building work is completed? If so, how long will that take? How is the occupation process to be managed? Who decides who goes where? Provision for all these activities must be made in the overall programme and budget.

COMMISSIONING

Discuss with the design team what equipment will need to be managed once the building is handed over. If you already have a facilities manager or someone who will take responsibility for this, make sure that they are included in the initial briefing and involved in the arrangements for testing and handing over. Training, or the appointment of additional staff may be required.

The builder and specialist installers are normally responsible for testing, and making sure that equipment is working satisfactorily before handover. Although they usually retain responsibility for its proper functioning for one year after practical completion, this does not normally include day to day management and maintenance. Full instructions, essential maintenance tools and spares should be supplied for you to do this. If the equipment is complex, familiarisation needs to take place before handover .

ARRANGEMENTS

The handover process must include arrangements for your assuming responsibilities, including:

Procedures
   recording, reporting and dealing with defects as they occur, including access arrangements.

Maintenance and servicing equipment and installation
   heating systems, ventilation and air conditioning plant, lifts, escalators, hoists, mechanical fittings, security systems, fire alarms and fire fighting equipment, control systems, telephone and communications.

Insurances
   insurance cover for the building, the equipment and its contents

Reading meters
   notification of transfer to new building owner

You require essential certificates relating to your building and its equipment. These include:

Compliance with regulations
   Planning, Listed Building , Building Regulations, Means of Escape, Licensed premises, Health and Safety Plan, test certificates for electrical and mechanical installations, gas, water, electricity, telephones

Guarantees and warranties
   for specialist installations or work not covered under the builder's general liability

You will also take over loose equipment:
   keys, loose fittings, tools, spares, including schedules

The content of the Owners Manual will depend upon your needs but should include the following basic material:

Record information
   the approved design drawings, as-built drawings, specifications and performance standards, schedules of equipment and operating instructions, name and manufacture of principal materials, and maintenance advice

APPENDIX 7
CONTRACTS & ARRANGEMENTS

STANDARD FORMS OF BUILDING CONTRACT

A variety of standard forms of contract have been published covering most of the commonly used procurement arrangements. The use, without amendment, of a commonly used standard form has clear advantages in forms of familiarity to the industry and established case law.

However, many claims and counter-claims are made regarding the merits and disadvantages of individual forms; you should seek expert advice, and consider carefully which contract is most suited to your particular project.

Before you enter a commitment to build, it is essential that you share with your advisers and intended builder a clear view of roles, responsibilities and risks in the project, and how they are expressed in the contract.

Standard forms are listed below according to publisher.

JOINT CONTRACTS TRIBUNAL

Standard Form of Building Contract
1980 Edition (JCT 80)

This is one of the most widely used forms for major designer-led building contracts. It is available with or without quantities, for use where full information is available at the time of tendering, or with approximate quantities if the building is not fully designed and measured. Time is an essential part of the contract. The contract is administered by either an architect or contract administrator. Specific and detailed provisions are made for nominating subcontractors and suppliers who are required to enter into complementary standard subcontracts.

Supplements exist to extend its scope for sectional completion allowing phasing of the works and for introducing an element of contractor's (builder's) design.

Separate editions are available for Local Authority and Private use.

Agreement for Minor Building Works
1980 Edition (MW 80)

This is a straightforward fixed price lump sum contract for small and simple designer-led projects of short duration. It is not available for use with quantities but can be scheduled and priced to afford a degree of cost control. Time is an essential part of the contract. The contract is administered by the architect/ supervising officer. No supplements are available to extend the range of the contract nor is there provision for nominated subcontract arrangements.

Not suitable for use in Scotland without alteration

Intermediate Form of Building Contract
for works of simple content
1984 Edition (IFC 84)

A mid-range lump sum contract designed to be used for relatively simple designer-led projects without complex service installations. It may be used by either public or private sectors, with or without quantities but the job must be fully designed at tender stage. The contract is administered either by an architect or contract administrator. Time is an essential part of the contract and should not exceed 12 months. Subcontractors may be named, but not nominated. Supplements exist to allow for sectional completion.

Not suitable for use in Scotland without alteration

Standard Form of Management Contract
1987 Edition (MC 87)

The only standard form of contract available for management contracting. Complementary arrangements for works contracts are included and integrated with main contract conditions.

Standard Form of Building Contract
With Contractor's Design 1981 Edition (WCD 81)

This form is intended for use where the builder takes full responsibility for the design, but allows flexibility in who actually undertakes design. Care needs to be taken in defining the responsibility where the client has a substantial input. Time is essential to the contract. The contract gives right of access to the employer's agent but makes no provision for supervision of the quality of the works.

Standard Form of Prime Cost Contract
1992 (PCC 92)

For work to be carried out on a cost reimbursement basis, with a fixed or percentage fee for the builders overheads and profit. Nomination of subcontractors is possible.

WARRANTIES

The JCT has published standard forms of collateral warranties, between both professional advisers ('consultants') and builders ('contractors') on one hand, and funders, purchasers and tenants on the other. They are suitable for use with the JCT 80, IFC84 and WCD81 forms.

The standard forms with JCT80 for nomination of subcontractors and suppliers include a warranty for design and performance direct to the client. If the form is not used, you should ensure that comparable arrangements are made to cover the work of all specialists.

SCOTTISH BUILDING CONTRACT COMMITTEE

Because of differences in Scottish law some of the standard contracts are unsuitable for use without adaptations. SBCC Minor Works is intended for use in Scotland. Larger works have to be undertaken using the JCT 80 with Scottish supplements

ASSOCIATION OF CONSULTANT ARCHITECTS

The ACA Form of Building Agreement 1982 Second edition 1984 (ACA form)

A lump sum contract intended for any size or type of project though probably best suited to middle range jobs. For use by private or public sectors it is not as widely used as the JCT contracts. It may be used with or without quantities and is capable of considerable flexibility through the use of option clauses. These allow for both the traditional designer led arrangements and for the builder to take some responsibility for design. They also provide for more detailed conditions with respect to time. Can be used with the BPF system (see below).

ARCHITECTS AND SURVEYORS INSTITUTE

The ASI (formed by the amalgamation of the Faculty of Architects and Surveyors and the Construction Surveyors Institute) publishes standard forms for designer-led projects used largely by its own members.

ASI Minor Works Contract (1980)

Intended for very small works. A fixed price contract based upon drawings and specifications. There is no provision for quantities.

ASI Small Works Contract (1981)

Fixed price or fluctuating, lump sum contract which can be extended by supplementary conditions to be used with quantities. No provision for nomination.

ASI Building Contract (1986)

Intended for larger or more complex work. A lump sum contract which may be used with or without quantities. Provision for nominating subcontractors and suppliers.

INSTITUTION OF CIVIL ENGINEERS

The ICE Conditions of Contract Sixth Edition 1991

This is the major form for use with civil engineering works and is based on tender drawings, specification and estimated quantities. The work is subject to remeasurement as it proceeds. Time is an essential part of the contract which is administered by the engineer. Only available in Approximate Quantities form

The ICE Conditions of Contract for Minor Works First edition 1988 (ICE Minor Works Form)

A straightforward contract for small civil engineering works of short duration. Can be used with quantities but more usually where remeasurement is anticipated.

Conditions of Contract for Design and Construct, 1992

The standard form for design and build projects of a civil engineering nature. It replaces the role of the independent 'engineer' with that of 'employer's representative' who acts entirely on behalf of the client. There is no provision for a 'resident engineer' to act as inspector. It includes compulsory conciliation procedures.

New Engineering Contract (NEC)

The NEC is intended to facilitate good management by motivating each of the participants to manage their own contribution. It is claimed to be sufficiently flexible for use in:

- projects involving any combination of engineering and construction disciplines
- large and small projects
- traditional or management-based procurement arrangements
- contracts with or without bills of quantities
- contracts with design carried out by the Contractor in part, entirely or not at all
- contracts with the proportion of work subcontracted from zero to 100%
- cost reimbursable and target cost contracts

Experience of the NEC to date is limited and confined to a small number of clients

THE BRITISH PROPERTY FEDERATION
The British Property Federation (BPF) System

The British Property Federation is an organisation which represents most of the major property developers in the UK. The BPF System published in 1983 is a client- led project management system

The BPF System was devised to produce buildings more quickly and cheaply, by removing unnecessary obstacles to progress, avoiding overlap of effort between the different contributors to the construction process and by focusing on value for money. The main features of the system are:

- the separation of the overall project management function from both designer and builder and placing it with a technically expert client manager known as the client's representative.
- only the client's representative is empowered to give instructions on behalf of the client.
- a single design leader is designated to coordinate the design stage of the project until a contractor is appointed. The design leader is subsequently retained in an advisory capacity.
- encouragement of the early appointment of the contractor, who is expected to take design responsibility for a major element of the building.
- The appointment of a supervisor during the construction stage with responsibility for monitoring standards for the client's representative and design leader.

The System is fully described in the BPF Manual and is intended to be used primarily with its own integrated documentation. It is also capable of some adaptation for use with other systems, such as construction management though the documentation requires alteration to do this.

The BPF recommends the use of its own tailored contract documentation based on the ACA form but the system can be used in conjunction with JCT WCD81

TBV CONSULT

PSA/1 with quantities (June 1994)

This form was developed from GC/Works/1 Edition 3, for building and civil engineering projects in both private and public sectors. It is for use with bills of quantities, where all or most of the quantitites are firm, giving a lump sum contract subject to adjustment for variations ordered. It provides for:
- payment according to stage payment chart and programme
- pre-agreement of prices and variations
- defined single point responsibility of the project manager
- specification of the desired level of design ability

PSA/1 contains all ancillary documents usually needed, such as collateral warranties and performance bonds.

No experience in its use has been built up.

STANDARD TERMS OF ENGAGEMENT FOR ADVISERS

The more commonly used standard terms of engagement are listed below.

Association of Consulting Engineers

ACE Terms of Engagement 1995

A   Engineer as lead consultant
B   Engineer employed direct by the client, but not as lead consultant
C   Engineer employed by design and build contractor
D   Report and advisory work
E   Project management
F   Planning supervisor (under CDM regulations)

Association of Project Managers

Terms of engagement for project managers 1995

Institution of Civil Engineers

Professional Services Contract 1994 - covers all professional services, intended for use with New Engineering Contract (NEC).

Royal Institute of British Architects

RIBA Standard Form of Agreement for the Appointment of an Architect 1992 (SFA/92), plus additional schedules of services for:

- historic buildings
- community architecture
- design and build procurement

Royal Institution of Chartered Surveyors

RICS Agreement for the appointment of a quantity surveyor, 1992
RICS Agreement for the appointment of a Chartered Building Surveyor 1992
Project Management Agreement and Conditions of Engagement 1992

The following offer further information about the main procurement options available today:

CIRIA publications

Target and cost Reimbursable Construction Contacts	J G Perry P A Thompson M Wright	CIRIA R85	1982
Management Contracting		CIRIA R100	1983
Roles Responsibilities and Risks in Management Contracting	B Curtis S Ward C Clayton	CIRIA SP81	1991
Value by Competition A Guide to the Competitive Procurement of Consultancy Services for Construction.	JN Connaughton	CIRIA SP117	1995
Control of Risk A Guide to the Systematic Management of Risk in Construction	P Godfrey	CIRIA SP	1995
Value Management in UK Practice	JN Connaughton S Green	CIRIA SP	Due 1996
CDM Regulations Case Study Guidance for Designers, an Interim Report		CIRIA Report R!45	1995

Other publications

An Introduction to Building Procurement Systems	J W E Masterman	Spon	1992
Building Procurement	Alan Turner	Macmillan Education Ltd	1990
Building Procurement Systems	James Franks	CIOB	1990
Client's Guide to Building	Ray Cecil	Legal Studies Publishing	1993
Design & Build Contract Practice	Dennis Turner	Longman	1986
Design & Build Explained	David Janssens	Macmillan Education Ltd	1990
The BPF System	BPF	The BPF Ltd	1983
Thinking of Building?		The Building Round Table Ltd	1995
Which Contract?	H Clamp S Cox	RIBA	1989